BARLOWE'S GUIDE TO
fantasy

BARLOWE'S GUIDE TO
fantasy

Wayne Douglas Barlowe
with text by **Neil Duskis**

HarperPrism

This book is for you, Hillary Cameron Barlowe—
imp, elf, and princess all rolled into one.
Knowing you makes me believe in magic.
—*Wayne Douglas Barlowe*

HarperPaperbacks
A Division of HarperCollins*Publishers*
10 East 53rd Street, New York, N.Y. 10022-5299

Copyright © 1996 by Wayne Douglas Barlowe
Art copyright © 1996 by Wayne Douglas Barlowe

HarperPrism is an imprint of HarperPaperbacks.
HarperCollins®, ■®, HarperPaperbacks™, and HarperPrism®
are trademarks of HarperCollins*Publishers* Inc.

HarperPaperbacks may be purchased for educational, business,
or sales promotional use. For information, please write:
Special Markets Department, HarperCollins*Publishers,*
10 East 53rd Street, New York, N.Y. 10022-5299.

Printed in the United States of America

First printing: November 1996

Library of Congress Cataloging-in-Publication Data

Barlowe, Wayne Douglas.
    [Guide to fantasy]
    Barlowe's guide to fantasy/Wayne Douglas Barlowe; with text by Neil Duskis.
       p.   cm.
    ISBN: 0-06-105238-8 (hc). — ISBN: 0-06-100817-6 (pbk.)
    1. Barlowe, Wayne Douglas—Themes, motives. 2. Science fiction—
    Illustrations. 3. Fantasy in art. 4. Illustration of books—20th century—
    United States. I. Duskis, Neil. II. Title.
NC975.5.B36A4 1996
741 .64ʹ092--dc20   96-3056
                                               CIP

Visit HarperPaperbacks on the World Wide Web at
http://www.harpercollins.com/paperbacks

96 97 98 99 ❖ 10 9 8 7 6 5 4 3 2 1

Acknowledgments

Without any doubt, my first and greatest thanks must go to my incredibly wonderful and patient wife, Shawna McCarthy. I couldn't have done this book without her support and help. My daughters, Cayley and Hillary, also contributed their love and senses of wonder, two more elements that were essential to me.

Neil Duskis, my researcher and coauthor, has been a dear friend, an indefatigable resource, a patient and professional collaborator, an objective and valued critic, and a delight to work with. No amount of thanks can express my gratitude to him.

This book could not have been done without the consent of its many living authors. To them I offer deep thanks.

Special thanks to John Silbersack and Caitlin Blasdell for their interest in the book from the beginning and their continued help as it took shape.

Ellen Datlow must top the list of people peripheral to the project who gave invaluable aid. Thanks so much, Ellen.

Thanks to my agent, Russell Galen, who is simply the best there is.

Thanks to Jim Cowan, Neil Gordon, Broeck Steadman, and Phil Tippett for their friendship and support.

Thanks also to Thomas Dixon for allowing me to Mort-ify him.

Finally, and as always, I want to thank my immediate family, Sy, Dorothea, and Amy for their warmth, understanding and love.

—*Wayne Douglas Barlowe*

I would like to thank my wife Harriet, my brother Robert, sister-in-law Gregg and my mother and stepfather, for their continuing love and support. A special thanks to Wayne Barlowe, artist, visionary, and friend.

—*Neil Duskis*

Table of Contents

Foreword

Great imaginations are like great generals: they storm cities, defend realms, and change the course of history.

Almost twenty years ago, when I was a fledgling editor with Berkley Books (then a fledgling company), we needed an artist to paint a cover for an unusual Frank Herbert novel, not one of his immortal Dune books but a "maverick" that didn't fit any known mold. The book was *Soul Catcher*, and the solution, by an almost-unknown named Wayne Barlowe, was an elegant and evocative Native American design that captured the shamanistic spirit of Herbert's tale as effectively as the subject of the book snagged its own elusive quarry.

As impressed as I was by the sophistication of Barlowe's work, I was even more taken by the depth of its influences. His was a traditional kind of originality, reaching back to draw from a wellspring of painterly naturalism that was untapped by and perhaps even unknown to most of the fantasy artists in New York publishing circles. It was so old it was new.

In those days science fiction publishing was coming out of its "modernist" period, when the design of paperback covers had been influenced, indeed dictated, by the great Richard Powers (who died just this year—1996). Power's Dali-esque abstractions had done the genre a great service, sweeping away the rocket ships, ray guns, and brass bras of SF's adolescence. But now another spirit was needed for another age, something akin to the speculative SF that was being created. Barlowe seemed to be pointing in the right direction.

Wayne Barlowe solved more problems for us those days, including the spectacular cover for Michael Moorcock's *Chronicles of Corum*; and if I had paid closer attention I would not have been surprised to find that he could render animals and creatures with an uncanny accuracy. I should certainly not have been surprised by the brilliant success of *Barlowe's Guide to Extraterrestrials*.

But I was; like the rest of the SF world, I was stunned and astonished. I am still astonished, almost twenty years later when I look back at this classic work. Barlowe's ground-breaking, mind-blowing, genre-bending illustrations gave form, substance, and solidity to the imaginative creations of some of the greatest authors in the field, rendering the elusive heart of science fiction tangible and concrete as it had never been before.

And not a moment too soon. It was no mistake that Barlowe's first "Guide" came along at about the time of the hit film *Star Wars*. Cinema seemed determined to overshadow print, to prove that ours was a cinematic and not a literary genre; that books were (at best) second-string stuff. It was left to an artist in the field, one of the most literate and educated (indeed, how many painters dedicate their work to an English travel essayist?) to give the fictional creations of classic science fiction the detail and solidity, the form and substance they needed to keep from being blown away by the Big Wind from Hollywood.

Barlowe made SF real in a new way. All of us who live and breathe and love speculative literature owe Wayne an incalculable debt for his first "Guide." He not only defended our realm, he peopled it with some of the most vivid and amazing creations that ever walked, crawled, or slithered through our collective imagination. Distinguished authors were delighted, amazed (and sometimes appalled) to find their bizarre creations—the Salaman, the Polarian, the Garnishee—rendered as exactingly and lovingly as Audubon's finches.

Barlowe's first "Guide" became one of the rare works in American literature to be nominated both for the Hugo and the American Book Award. Since that day, this most productive of artists has gone on to create more than 300 book and magazine covers, as well as paintings for *Time, Life,* and *Newsweek.* His most personal creations, both as a writer *and* an artist, came to the fore in his acclaimed faux-Darwinian masterpiece *Expedition,* in which he created with the exactitude of a naturalist an entire alien ecology.

But now the circle has gone full turn, and Barlowe is here with his second "Guide." What the first "Guide" did for SF, this one promises to do for SF's lovely and terrifying sister, Fantasy, providing definitive portrayals of the field's most awesome monsters and haunting creatures.

For this long-awaited delight, this inimitable pleasure and this timely boon, I, along with others in the field, can only say—

Thanks.

—*John Silbersack*
Editor-in-Chief, HarperPrism

Introduction

No endeavor that humanity engages in is as limitless in its freedom and potential as the creation of fantasy. Whether or not you regard mythology, or the satiric works of Swift, or the gently mad creations of Carroll as fantasy, the unarguable truth is that they have all sprung from the inventive minds of people intent on creating new worlds—worlds not based on the pure rationalism of science.

What is it about fantasy that has so captivated the minds of people since time began? Why have *Beowulf* and *Gilgamesh* and *The Odyssey* endured thousands of years of reading? What qualities do certain fantasy characters possess that compel people to identify with them for centuries? I think that through fantasy, people—both primitive and civilized—have the sudden ability to ask for and be granted all things. The realm of fantasy is one in which absolutely anything can and does happen. And as such, it is as fulfilling as anything can be.

As a young man I read as much good old fantasy as I could lay my hands on. Eddison, Dunsany, Hodgson, and Lindsay, to name a few, were my guides to those fertile fields of enchantment and they rarely let me down. I've gone back to their worlds, to Eddison's Mercury, Hodgson's House, and Lindsay's Tormance, and the thrill, undiminished by years, is always there.

For me the appeal was in the details, the wonderfully descriptive prose that painted vivid pictures in my mind that, I am sure, were pale in comparison with the authors' rich visions. And it is all of these details, so lovingly created, that come together to convince the reader that these worlds are real.

A world, however well realized, is nothing without characters to populate it. Fantasy is rich in vividly portrayed beings whose presences resonate long after a book is put down. This book is full of just those kinds of unforgettable creations. The people and beings you will meet within these pages are there because they have either endured the test of time or will. I had a difficult task, not dissimilar from the task I had nearly twenty years ago with *Barlowe's Guide to Extraterrestrials*, winnowing through the enormity of the literature. Early on, I decided to rule out mythological figures. Out of respect for religions, both living and dead, I studiously avoided any depictions of nonsecular characters. Even with this omission, I felt that the historical boundaries of fantasy were somewhat greater than science fiction. The task of selection proved to be more of a challenge than its predecessor.

Once my researcher, Neil, and I arrived at those characters that were to be included, the real work began. As with *Extraterrestrials* I carefully analyzed the author's words. Only after I felt that I had interpreted their meanings, both literally and contextually, did I feel that I could pick up my brush. On purely imagined creatures I was on my own. For instance, in imagining a Trolloc's clan badge I could answer to my own aesthetic. Historically framed characters, however, were another problem altogether. I was then confronted with a surprising amount of necessary historical research; fantasy authors are notoriously aware of history. From Bran Mak Morn's Pictish dagger to the tengu's hat, I have striven for accuracy. If I have failed at any point the blame is mine, and mine alone.

An odd painting technique shift occurred, almost from the outset, while I worked on this *Guide to Fantasy*. Formerly, I worked in an opaque fashion with my acrylics; all of *Extraterrestrials* was rendered in this way. When I commenced work on this book I suddenly felt a need to change the very laying on of paint and as a result I began to work within a more traditional, English watercolor style. Thin, worked-up washes replaced opaque blocking-in of forms. Somehow this seemed more appropriate to the subject. Unfortunately, it also doubled the rendering time. I hope that this decision was correct and that the detail and luminosity that I strived for is ultimately rewarding.

From the beginning I wanted *Barlowe's Guide to Fantasy* to have a broader scope than its predecessor. Aliens, in their science fiction incarnations, are relatively new to literature. Fantastic beings are just the opposite; they have been with us since the beginning of recorded history. That fact forced me to broaden the scope of this book. This, I believe, has been achieved with the inclusion of not only ancient archetypes but also creations from the last century. A book of this kind would be nothing without acknowledging the role that Edgar Allen Poe, for example, played in the literature of the fantastic. And how could one ignore the great turn-of-the-century fantasists who so brilliantly influenced today's writers? Fantasy is not a phenomenon of the second half of our century. We are merely enjoying its richest period, to date.

I hope you enjoy this guide to fantasy; it has taken me from one wonderful world to another. May it do the same for you.

—*Wayne Barlowe*

BARLOWE'S GUIDE TO
fantasy

THE WORLD Millions of years in the future the earth has changed beyond recognition. Continents and weather patterns have shifted, altering the face of the planet. Vast urban centers, like Nessus, contain structures so old no one remembers their original functions.

Advanced technologies, like star flight, coexist with primitive religious rites. Much of the known world is ruled by an all-powerful tyrant, given the title of Autarch.

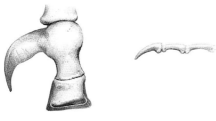

Comparison of Alzabo's claw with a Kodiak bear's claw

HISTORY Many professions have reverted to an almost-medieval system where new members are apprenticed during childhood. Among the most powerful of these guilds are the Torturers, who execute criminals and conduct interrogations for the Autarch. Easily identifiable by their leather masks and dark cloaks, they are universally feared as bringers of pain and suffering.

Severian, an orphan raised by the Torturers, is on the verge of obtaining his journeyman's mask, when he is banished from the order for showing mercy to a political prisoner. Expelled from Nessus, Severian sets out on a journey that will take him through war-torn lands to the Citadel of the Autarch.

During the course of his travels he acquires Terminus Est, a finely crafted sword, and the Claw, a mysterious gem, which may have the power to raise the dead. These objects will help Severian withstand numerous encounters with human foes and strange beasts, like the Alzabo.

PHYSICAL CHARACTERISTICS Alzabos are deadly alien creatures brought to earth by interstellar voyagers to replace extinct terrestrial species. Haunting isolated areas, they survive by preying on the unwary. While information on their home world is sketchy, their red fur and preference for mountainous regions, suggest it must have been a cold place.

Fearsome predators with a taste for human flesh, Alzabos tear apart their prey with sharp talons and enormous jaws. They are voracious eaters who can devour and digest a full-grown man in a matter of moments.

Alzabos' most frightening trait is their ability to absorb, through some unknown process, the memories of those they kill. This allows the creatures to mimic human speech and thought patterns, making them even more dangerous.

Lateral view of Alzabo showing hair pattern and dorsal crest

ALZABO

SOURCE:
The Sword of the Lictor
Gene Wolfe

SERIES:
The Book of the New Sun

THE WORLD The great age of exploration and colonization wrought great changes in Africa. Long-established cultures were destroyed by outsiders searching for slaves and plunder.

Somewhere, outside a small village far removed from the events of this turbulent era, lived a woman named Anyanwu. Gifted with extraordinary powers, she would be forced to abandon her homeland for the new world.

HISTORY Born in ancient Nubia, Doro has survived for centuries by transferring his mind from one host body to another. Obsessed with the desire to create a race of superhumans, he searches the world for individuals with exceptional abilities.

Doro gathers his finds in isolated communities, protecting and providing for them. Most, who have been persecuted as witches, are only too glad to accept his hospitality. In return they are selectively bred to enhance their offspring's psychic abilities.

When he stumbles across Anyanwu in a remote part of Africa, Doro realizes he has finally encountered someone whose powers rival his own. Doro forces her to accompany him to a frontier town in North America. But he will soon learn that Anyanwu will be no one's slave.

PHYSICAL CHARACTERISTICS Anyanwu's family has a long history of extrasensory powers. Venerated as a healer by the people of her village, she is, like Doro, virtually immortal.

Blessed with almost-magical control of her body, Anyanwu can purge disease organisms and poisons from her system at will. When wounded, her flesh heals instantaneously, rendering her nearly impossible to kill.

Anyanwu's transforming hand

Mistress of many forms, Anyanwu can transform herself into a leopard, eagle, wolf, or dolphin. Becoming a creature she has never been before requires practice, and Anyanwu sometimes experiments with forming portions of the beast's anatomy before transforming completely.

Unlike Doro, who views others as objects to be used in his grand design, Anyanwu has a highly developed moral sense. Fiercely loyal to her children, she will take whatever measures are necessary to protect them.

ANYANWU

SOURCE:
Wild Seed
Octavia E. Butler

SERIES:
The Patternist Novels

THE WORLD In the dim past, before the English came, India was a land of wonder and mystery. Its primal forests and dense jungles were home to strange creatures unlike any on earth. While many were kindly disposed toward humanity, others, like the Baital, were to be avoided at all costs.

HISTORY One of the greatest kings, or rajas, of this lost age was Vikram. Warrior and sage, Vikram upheld the righteous and punished the wicked without mercy. Throughout the course of his life, Vikram had many great adventures, but none as strange as his encounter with the Baital.

Baital's opened wing

Lured to a burial ground by a pledge, the mysterious jogi, Shanta-Shil, Vikram, and his son, Prince Dharma Dhwaj, found themselves surrounded by ghouls and demons. Shanta-Shil instructed the king to capture a Baital, or vampire, roosting in a nearby tree and bring it to him.

Every time Vikram laid hands on the creature it quickly slipped from his grasp. As the king and his son soon discovered, the Baital was a master storyteller, with a unique philosophy of life. Throughout the night, the vampire spun tales of love and betrayal, while Vikram and Dhwaj listened spellbound, finally learning Shanta-Shil's true intent.

PHYSICAL CHARACTERISTICS Baitals are evil spirits with the power to resurrect the dead. Drawing sustenance from human blood, they often assume a batlike shape and hang from tree limbs by their toes, waiting to drain unsuspecting travelers dry.

Those who have survived encounters with Baitals never forget their untwinkling eyes and corpse-cold skin, which is clammy to the touch. Able to converse with humans, Baitals are known for their dry wit and sense of irony.

THE WORLD Arbonne and Gorhaut, two nations in a world similar to Medieval Europe, are radically different places. Gorhaut is a cold land, ruled by a mad king and his court of bloodthirsty aristocrats. Women are treated like property and routinely abused.

Arbonne, which boasts a milder clime, is a center of music and art. Equality of the sexes is taken for granted, and troubadours are revered.

A wolf mask of the High Priestess of Rian

HISTORY Although Blaise de Garsenc was born into one of the most powerful families in Gorhaut, his social status has never brought him happiness. Tired of being manipulated by his amoral father, Blaise decides to leave.

Traveling south to Arbonne, de Garsenc uses his considerable military skills to find work as a mercenary. On a mission to an island sacred to Rian, Arbonne's patron goddess, he encounters the mysterious Beatritz de Barbentain, who seems able to read his thoughts.

Just as he begins to feel at home, a crisis erupts. Urged on by de Garsenc's father, the king of Gorhaut is about to invade Arbonne, and only Blaise can lead his adopted land's armies to victory.

PHYSICAL CHARACTERISTICS A High Priestess of Rian, Beatritz de Barbentain has willingly sacrificed her sight for knowledge. Clad in plain garments, she is accompanied by a white owl, which may be her familiar or a symbol of office. The living embodiment of Rian's authority, she is an imposing figure who commands attention.

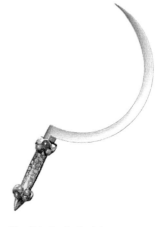

Rian Priestess's ritual dagger

Under certain conditions, Beatritz can read minds and heal wounds no physician can cure. The daughter of Countess Signe, who rules Arbonne, she is a skilled politician and one of her mother's most valued councilors.

BEATRITZ DE BARBENTAIN

SOURCE:
A Song for Arbonne
Guy Gavriel Kay

THE WORLD In the dark years after the fall of the Roman Empire, Britain was pillaged by marauders from across the Channel, including the Saxon hordes. These fierce warrior tribes would become locked in a bitter struggle with King Arthur for control of the British Isles.

Achilles's spear and shield

HISTORY Yearning for a weapon which will terrorize his Saxon foes, Arthur commands Merlin to summon a dragon. Unfortunately, conjuring up such a creature is no easy task. Certain items, like the skull of a loch-swimmer, the nearly extinct serpentine reptiles which inhabit the lakes of Ireland, are required.

Mael, a mercenary serving in the king's army, is coerced into procuring the remains Merlin needs. During his travels in Ireland he encounters Veleda, a mysterious woman who may be a witch. They become lovers, and she warns him the creature Merlin plans to unleash will grow indefinitely, threatening all life on earth.

After several close calls, Mael locates the skull and returns to Britain with Veleda. The mercenary delivers it to a delighted Merlin, who is eager to proceed with the task at hand.

At Veleda's urging, Mael and his Danish companion Starkad embark on a journey through hostile Saxon territory in search of the Spear and Shield of Achil. These legendary artifacts, forged before the Trojan Wars, have the power to destroy the dragon.

Captured by a band of Saxon warriors, Mael learns the Shield is hidden in a nearby cistern with the corpse of a chieftain named Biargram Ironhand. But the information does him little good when he is buried alive with Biargram's unquiet ghost.

PHYSICAL CHARACTERISTICS A powerful warlord in life, Biargram Ironhand was unlucky enough to own the Spear and Shield of Achil. For the warlock Ceadwalla coveted these magical weapons and was willing to kill to get them.

Ceadwalla intimidated Biargram into surrendering the Spear, then slew him by magical means when he refused to part with the Shield. But Ironhand cannot rest in peace. Each night at moonrise his vengeful corpse awakens to wreak havoc on the living.

Animated by some unknown force, Biargram prowls the narrow confines of his tomb. Still clad in his chieftain's finery, Ironhand's flesh has become rock hard. His chilling facial expression reveals the hatred he bears to the living. Only the setting of the moon saves Mael from being torn apart by the bloodthirsty zombie.

BIARGRAM IRONHAND

SOURCE:
The Dragon Lord
David Drake

THE WORLD When the Romans invaded Britain during the first century, they ventured northward into the dense forests and snowy hills of what is now Scotland. It was in the depths of this wild land that they encountered a small, dark people known as Picts.

Led by their warrior king, Bran Mak Morn, the Picts made the legions pay in blood for every inch of ground they took.

Their relentless attacks forced the Romans to construct Hadrian's Wall, a defensive barrier which stands to this day.

Bran's favorite dirk

HISTORY An ancient people who could trace their history back to the days before Atlantis sank, the Picts had fallen upon hard times by the dawn of the Roman era. Only the iron will of their king and the few scraps of knowledge retained by their tribal shamans kept them from reverting to complete savagery.

Unable to defeat the numerically superior Romans in pitched battle, Bran was often forced to use ancient magics against them. On one occasion, Mak Morn forged an unholy alliance with the Worms of the Earth, a humanoid race dwelling beneath the moors of the high country, to win a crucial battle.

PHYSICAL CHARACTERISTICS Of medium build, lithe, and muscular, Bran has the dark hair and skin characteristic of his people. Dressed for battle, in a wolfskin mantle and light mail, he is armed with a short sword.

The red jewel set in his iron crown was a gift from Kull, a great Atlantean emperor, to one of Mak Morn's distant ancestors. Passed from father to son, it has come to represent the Picts' former glory.

Bran was a great swordsman, whose actions were governed by a strict code of honor. A stern ruler, he was not without compassion and often spared those who fought valiantly against him.

Mak Morn dreamed of restoring his people's lost greatness but was unable to do so. Shortly after his death, the Picts slipped into barbarism and were absorbed by the Scots.

BRAN MAK MORN

SOURCE:
Bran Mak Morn
Robert E. Howard

THE WORLD Gwynedd is a unique feudal state. For centuries this mountain kingdom has been home to two races, ordinary humans and Deryni, an ancient folk who possess powers that can only be described as supernatural.

While they resemble ordinary mortals, the Deryni can summon fearsome creatures from other dimensions and perform miraculous acts of healing. Needless to say, those without these abilities often view them with fear.

Despite mutual suspicion, the Deryni have always managed to coexist with their human neighbors. But the fragile peace between the two groups is threatened with the accession of King Imre Festil to the throne.

The MacRorie Arms

HISTORY In the not-so-distant past, Imre's ancestors usurped the crown from the human Haldanes, establishing a Deryni dynasty. While his predecessors were careful not to antagonize their non-Deryni subjects, Imre has no such qualms. The king's actions, ordering brutal reprisals for any crime against a Deryni and flaunting an incestuous relationship with his sister, trigger widespread discontent.

One of those alienated by Imre's policies is Camber MacRorie, earl of Culdi. A Deryni scholar and former royal advisor, Camber finds himself torn between loyalty to the Festils and his personal beliefs.

When one of his sons discovers a long-forgotten Haldane heir living quietly in a monastery, Camber realizes Imre can be replaced. Now the stage is set for a brutal dynastic struggle, a battle in which Deryni magic will play a crucial role.

PHYSICAL CHARACTERISTICS A silver-haired, grey-eyed man in the prime of life, Camber is a rare combination of warrior, scholar, and politician. Dressed in the robes of a scholar, the earl carries an ancient volume of Deryni lore and a reading glass. Well-versed in magic, his skills include spells of disguise and the ability to use the ancient Deryni transfer portals, which provide instantaneous transportation between distant points.

Camber has always been a staunch advocate of human–Deryni coexistence. Unafraid to stand up for his beliefs, for justice, he will risk his life and the lives of those he holds dear.

CAMBER OF CULDI

SOURCE:
Camber of Culdi
Katherine Kurtz

SERIES:
The Deryni Chronicles

THE WORLD One lazy summer afternoon a long time ago, a little English girl named Alice was sitting by a riverbank. Bored, she caught a glimpse of a White Rabbit, who just happened to be carrying a pocket watch and wearing a waistcoat. Intrigued, Alice took off in pursuit, setting off on the adventure of a lifetime.

The Caterpillar's hand

HISTORY Alice followed the animal down a hole. Falling for what seemed like forever down a cupboard-lined shaft, our heroine landed without a bump.

She found herself in a strange underground world. After experimenting with potions that altered her size, Alice went exploring, and met many strange creatures, including a rather snooty Caterpillar. Of course being a clever, well-brought-up child, she managed to take everything in stride and come out all right in the end.

PHYSICAL CHARACTERISTICS Shortly after eating some mysterious cakes which reduce her to a mere three inches, Alice encounters a spiny-backed, hookah-smoking Caterpillar. This odd, blue creature engages Alice in a philosophical discussion about the nature of identity, then informs her she can control her growth by eating pieces of the mushroom he's perched on.

CATERPILLAR

SOURCE:
Alice's Adventures in Wonderland
Lewis Carroll

THE WORLD Since the dawn of time humanity has shared the planet with another species. Popularly known as fairies, they possess abilities that are beyond human understanding.

Near the end of the last century, for reasons known only to them, a community of fairy folk left Ireland and relocated to upstate New York. Establishing a unique relationship with the eccentric Drinkwater family, they devised a grand design which will change the course of history.

HISTORY Smoky Barnable has had a unique childhood. Raised by his rather odd father, he considers himself somewhat bohemian.

When Smoky's friend George Mouse introduces him to Daily Alice Drinkwater, it's love at first sight.

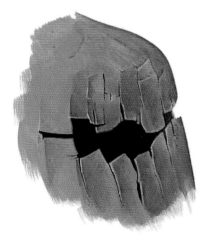

After a whirlwind courtship and strange marriage ceremony, Smoky moves into the Drinkwaters' Catskill home. Barnable soon discovers he's entered a magical world, where houses are gateways to other realms and people are transformed into animals. What Smoky doesn't realize is that the fairy folk have plans for his family, plans that include substituting a Changeling for his sister-in-law's child.

PHYSICAL CHARACTERISTICS The Changeling is an infant simulacrum, substituted at birth for one of the Drinkwater children by its fairy masters. Growing at an incredible pace, the Changeling rapidly develops into a sexless entity, wise beyond its years and hostile toward humanity.

Detail of broken skin revealing hollow interior

Not alive in any conventional sense, it appears to be some sort of hollow-bodied automaton, covered with leathery skin. Attracted to heat, the Changeling derives energy from fire and has been observed swallowing red-hot coals. One of the last of its kind, the Changeling's childlike appearance only makes it more repulsive.

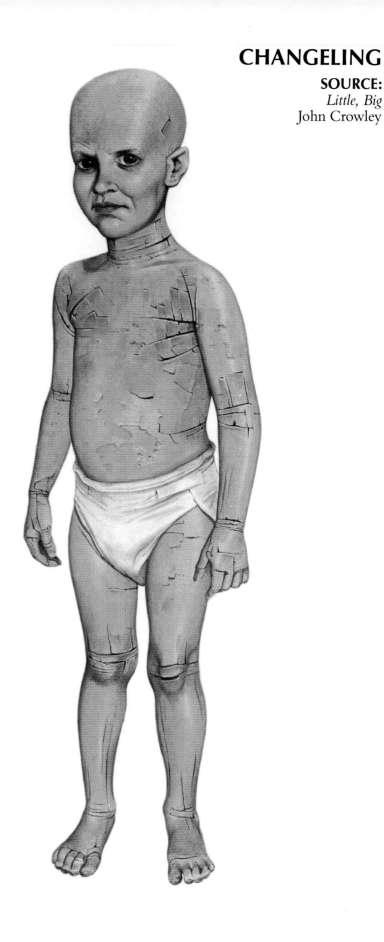

THE WORLD Aeons ago, in a forgotten age, the earth was flat. Magic was commonplace and a race of demigods, known as the Vazdru, amused themselves by meddling in human affairs.

It was a time of decadence, when power-hungry sorcerers made pacts with entities they could not control. Vast cities, whose glittering spires pierced the clouds, dotted the landscape, and strange cults flourished.

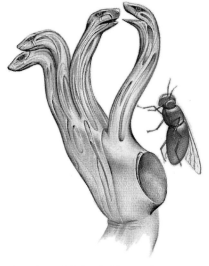

Chuz's brass right hand with stone fly

HISTORY The most powerful of the Vazdru were known as the Lords of Darkness. Their ranks included Azhrarn, who ruled the hours between dusk, and dawn but could not withstand sunlight; Uhlume, lord of death and the underworld; and Chuz, patron saint of the mad. Close enough in nature to be brothers, they often fought amongst themselves for reasons no mortal could understand.

While all the Lords of Darkness were terrifying presences, none was more feared than Chuz. Fickle as the state of mind he personified, Chuz was capable of both excessive kindness and sadistic cruelty. Also known as Prince Madness and Delusion's Master, he offered his acolytes the bliss of forgetfulness and the ecstasy of abandon.

PHYSICAL CHARACTERISTICS In keeping with his mercurial nature, one side of Chuz's face is strikingly handsome and the other is hideously shriveled. The palm of Prince Madness's left hand is black with long, red nails, while the right is concealed beneath a white glove.

In a similar manner, he has one bare foot and one shod foot. Chuz's bronze teeth and oddly colored eyes contribute to his terrifying aspect.

Clad in a dark purple robe adorned with glass fragments, Chuz carries a strange rattle and the jawbones of an ass. When shaken, the rattle produces a brain-shattering cacophony, which the jaws accompany with bizarre braying sounds.

CHUZ

SOURCE:
Delusion's Master
Tanith Lee

SERIES:
Tales from the Flat Earth

THE WORLD The Vadhagh were an ancient race who inhabited one small world in a universe of interconnecting realities, or planes. Known for their highly developed aesthetic sense and love of esoteric knowledge, they lived together in small, isolated, family groups.

For centuries the Vadhagh mistakenly ignored the human tribes, which they called Mabden, multiplying in the wilderness.

Banding together under the leadership of Glandyth-a-Krae, the Mabden united and slaughtered the Vadhagh in a genocidal frenzy.

Only one of the Vadhagh, Prince Corum Jhaelen Irsei, managed to survive. Captured and maimed, Corum escaped and lived to plan his revenge.

Typical Vadagh weapons

HISTORY Vowing to destroy Glandyth, Corum traveled to the island of the sorcerer Shool-an-Jyvan. Shool offered to replace the prince's lost body parts with the Eye of Rhynn and the Hand of Kwll. These magical prosthetics gave Corum the power to carry out his vengeance, but they came with a price.

In return, the wizard demanded Corum steal the heart of Arioch, a demigod whose power Shool coveted. Succeeding against all odds, the prince learned he is a key player in the never-ending struggle between Law and Chaos. Later in the course of his tortured life, Corum will discover that he is one of the many incarnations of the Eternal Champion, a hero reborn countless times on thousands of worlds.

PHYSICAL CHARACTERISTICS Tall and thin, with the rose-hued skin typical of his race, the prince moves with a grace humans find impossible to imitate. Like most Vadhagh, he is able to travel between different realities or planes at will.

Also known as the Prince in the Scarlet Robe because of his distinctive cloak, Corum is a striking figure. His helmet and spear are examples of the highly refined nature of Vadhagh craftsmanship.

The six-fingered, jeweled gauntlet called the Hand of Kwll, which Corum wears on his left arm, gives him superhuman strength and the power to detect hidden threats. His artificial right eye allows the prince to view events occurring in several different planes simultaneously. Relics of the elder gods, these items possess a will of their own and are determined to protect Corum at any cost.

CORUM JHAELEN IRSEI

SOURCE:
The Knight of the Swords
Michael Moorcock

SERIES:
The Chronicles of Corum

THE WORLD The only real place in a universe of infinite possibilities, Amber was created from primal chaos by its liege, Lord Oberon. Over time, the immortal sovereign has sired a brood of children whose chief preoccupations are intrigue and the pursuit of power.

All Oberon's descendants have the ability to travel between the parallel worlds or shadows surrounding Amber. To perfect this skill, they must master the Pattern, a strange maze in the depths of their ancestral castle.

While many of these shadows are similar to earth, others can be deadly. Perhaps the strangest is an alien landscape of moving rock, populated by humanoids with spurred hands.

HISTORY Returning home after centuries of exile, Corwin, a prince of Amber, finds himself involved in a battle for the throne. King Oberon has disappeared, leaving a dangerous power vacuum. Corwin's half brother, Eric, wants the crown and is willing to kill to get it.

"Firefly" form of Dara

Imprisoned under horrendous conditions after an unsuccessful bid to seize control of Amber, Corwin manages to escape. Fleeing from shadow to shadow, the prince encounters the Dark Circle.

A rift in the fabric of reality, the Circle is being used as a gateway by demonic creatures who destroy everything in their path. Corwin learns that the Circle's point of origin is the Courts of Chaos, a place of wild magic, but is unable to discern its true purpose.

Taking refuge in a world ruled by Benedict, a sibling with whom he is on decent terms, Corwin meets Dara. Claiming to be Benedict's granddaughter, Dara strikes up a relationship with Corwin, eventually seducing him.

The prince departs to raise an army to depose Eric. When he returns to Amber at the head of his troops, Corwin finds it under siege and discovers there's more to Dara than meets the eye.

PHYSICAL CHARACTERISTICS A mysterious woman who undergoes a remarkable metamorphosis, Dara's true nature becomes apparent when she secretly follows Corwin home and walks the Pattern. While the stunned prince watches, Dara is transformed into a goddesslike figure, with many different attributes, who prophesies Amber's destruction.

DARA

SOURCE:
The Guns of Avalon
Roger Zelazny

SERIES:
The Amber Novels

THE WORLD Darwath is a kingdom of great cities and high mountains, where magic is an art practiced by scholars, and technology operates on a primitive level. Separated from our world by a barrier called the Void, it is ruled by a fragile coalition of nobles and clerics.

HISTORY Thousands of years ago, Darwath was nearly destroyed by the Dark Ones, mysterious creatures who prowl the night in search of human prey. While the survivors eventually managed to drive off the invaders, over the ages the secret behind their victory has been lost.

Tucked mouth of the Dark One

Reappearing without warning, the Dark Ones rapidly overwhelm Darwath's defenders. Fearing the worst, the wizard Ingold flees to earth, taking the infant heir to the throne with him for safekeeping.

Prior to his journey, the wizard contacts Gil, a graduate student living in California, who has been plagued with dreams about Darwath. Gil agrees to help Ingold and arranges to meet him at an isolated desert location. When Gil gets there, she stumbles across Rudy, a young auto mechanic whose car has broken down nearby.

Ingold arrives on schedule. But the wizard is unaware he has been followed by a Dark One. Attacked, Ingold transports himself and his charge back home to escape, dragging Rudy and Gil along in the process. Marooned in an alien land, the two Americans find themselves thrust into Darwath's battle for survival.

PHYSICAL CHARACTERISTICS Nightmarish monsters who feed on blood and psychic energy, Dark Ones are deadly antagonists. Lighter than air and able to change size and shape at will, they swoop down on their prey from above. Those who have seen them and lived speak of shadowy clawed forms, with whiplike tails and acid-secreting, tentacle-ringed mouths.

Dark Ones abhor light and seldom venture out before nightfall. They are vulnerable to flame and bladed weapons, which can easily pierce their thin flesh.

Highly intelligent, Dark Ones dwell in huge underground nests, surviving on specially bred human cattle. They possess their own brand of magic, totally alien to human wizards, and what appears to be a near-telepathic rapport with one another.

DARK ONE

SOURCE:
The Time of the Dark
Barbara Hambly

SERIES:
The Darwath Trilogy

THE WORLD The Land is a miraculous place inhabited by giants and herds of wild horses called Ranyhyn. A world of great beauty, where the very earth has the power to heal, it is the scene of an eternal conflict between the forces of good and evil.

The Staff of Law

HISTORY Thomas Covenant is a bitter man. A successful author with a beautiful wife and new baby, his world fell apart when he was diagnosed with leprosy. Abandoned by family and friends, Covenant spends his days in isolation, unable to live and afraid to die.

Magically summoned to the Land, Thomas discovers he's been given a second chance. For the Land has the power to cure him, but in return, he must defend it against the satanic Lord Foul and his pawn, Drool Rockworm.

PHYSICAL CHARACTERISTICS Cavewights are troll-like creatures who inhabit the caverns beneath a long-dead volcano. Easily recognizable by their red eyes, thin limbs, and enormous hands, their powerful bodies harbor evil dispositions.

Cavewight society is dominated by Drool Rockworm, an ambitious figure whose discovery of the Staff of Law, a potent magical tool lost for centuries, allows him to control his peers. Manipulated by Lord Foul, a mysterious entity with godlike powers, Drool uses the Staff to locate the Illearth Stone.

The Stone, a rock fragment which gives off a mysterious green radiance, enables its bearer to alter natural laws and distort reality. But Drool does not understand the forces he is tampering with, and his misuse of the Staff and Illearth Stone will prematurely age and eventually destroy him.

DROOL ROCKWORM

SOURCE:
Lord Foul's Bane
Steven R. Donaldson

SERIES:
*The Chronicles of Thomas Covenant
the Unbeliever*

THE WORLD The sixteenth century was a time of turmoil. A disunited Christendom seemed unable to resist the growing power of the Ottoman Empire. Already in control of the Balkans, the Turks prepared to move westward into Austria.

HISTORY Brian Duffy is an Irish mercenary who has fought too many battles. Weary of looting and burning his way across Europe, he lays down his sword and accepts a bouncer's job at Zimmermann's Inn, a famed Vienna tavern.

Afrit Magical Pipe

Renowned for the best dark beer in Austria, Zimmermann's is, as Duffy discovers, an unusual place. Home to a strange collection of self-proclaimed wizards, the bar is owned by the eccentric Aurelianus Ambrosius. An odd character who smokes snakes instead of tobacco, Ambrosius keeps hinting he and Duffy have met before.

Things take a downward turn when the Turks lay siege to the city. Trapped inside with a host of desperate characters, Brian has to listen to Ambrosius theorize about how the battle is part of a supernatural struggle between the forces of "East and West."

To make matters worse, the Irishman's boss is convinced Duffy is the reincarnation of King Arthur, who has returned to aid the West in its hour of need. While this is not what Brian wants to hear, a series of encounters with supernatural creatures, like the hideous Eastern Afrits, forces him to confront his destiny.

PHYSICAL CHARACTERISTICS An unholy hybrid of man and bird, Eastern Afrits are winged humanoids whose muzzled faces and fish-like eyes render them terrifying to behold. Summoned by Ottoman sorcerers to serve their cause during the siege of Vienna, they are armed with razor-sharp scimitars and magical pipes. These mysterious instruments produce an unearthly music, used to beguile the Eastern Afrits' enemies.

Able to swoop down out of the clouds without warning, Afrits' flying ability makes them ideal for commando raids and assassinations. While they resemble demons escaped from some inner circle of hell, Afrits are flesh-and-blood creatures who can be wounded or killed. Their use of artifacts, odd cloglike footgear, and skill in battle suggest a high degree of intelligence.

THE WORLD Ryhope Wood is a large tract of virgin forest in the north of England. Long believed to be haunted, the truth about Ryhope is far stranger. The forest has the power to generate mythagos, life-forms drawn from the memories of those who enter it. Able to function independently, these creatures can become deadly to their creators.

Those who enter Ryhope soon discover that time flows differently there. What seems like a straight path may be a loop trail to nowhere. Inhabited by human and bestial mythagos drawn from cultures extending back to prehistory, the forest is an awesome place.

HISTORY Christian Huxley grew up near Ryhope and knows there's something strange about the Wood. Returning home for his father's funeral, Christian discovers that his older brother, Steven, has become obsessed with the forest.

Events spin out of control when both men find themselves embroiled in a dangerous rivalry over Guiwenneth, a beautiful female mythago. For the contest can only be resolved within Ryhope, where the strangely transformed spirit of their father will become a fourth player in the struggle.

PHYSICAL CHARACTERISTICS Mischievous entities who inhabit Ryhope, Elementals are associated with climatic disturbances. First observed by Christian in the vicinity of his family home, they are wraithlike creatures with noseless faces.

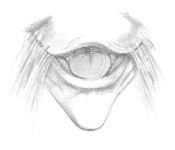

Elementals are able to make their bodies lighter than air and ride the wind. They can control the weather and use this ability to summon storms when it suits them. Capricious in nature, Elementals delight in prank playing, but can be deadly when roused.

They are often seen propelling the craft of Sorthalan, the "first boatman," through the sky. A powerful shaman, Sorthalan led his people across the ocean to the British Isles in the dim past and conquered the Elemental spirits native to the land.

Glowing interior of mouth

ELEMENTAL

SOURCE:
Mythago Wood
Robert Holdstock

SERIES:
The Ryhope Wood Novels

THE WORLD The Imajica is a universe of interconnected Dominions, worlds which border on, but are estranged from, our own. Populated by alien creatures, it is a place of wild magic and strange gods.

HISTORY Throughout history powerful mages known as Maestros have mastered the art of crossing the In Ovo, the deadly no-man's-land separating Earth from the Dominions. The greatest of these was Sartori, whose dream of uniting our world with the Imajica ended in disaster.

Unable to deal with the consequences of his failure, Sartori shed his identity and became Gentle, a womanizing art forger. Suffering from self-imposed amnesia for more than a century, he is shocked into partial remembrance by an encounter in contemporary Manhattan with a creature from the Dominions.

Known as Pie 'oh' Pah, this strange being seems able to alter its appearance at will. Once a close associate of the Maestro's, Pie was cast out by Sartori when his attempt to reconcile Earth with the Imajica soured.

A lateral view of a Gek-a-Gek head

With Pie as a guide, Gentle embarks on a tour of the Dominions. The Maestro's travels will restore his memory and prepare him for the great struggle which lies ahead.

PHYSICAL CHARACTERISTICS Gek-a-gek are demonic predators who dwell in the In Ovo. Flat-headed with large, clawed hands, they have streamlined forms that allow them to move quickly.

Though invisible in shadow, Gek-a-gek are rendered translucent in certain types of light. This unsettling effect reveals their internal structure, lending them a spectral appearance.

Driven by instinct rather than intelligence, Gek-a-gek rely on brute force to bring down their prey. Feared throughout the Imajica, they are seldom encountered outside the In Ovo.

THE WORLD Hampstead, Connecticut, looks like any other affluent bedroom community. Every weekday, a small army of men in three-piece suits boards the Manhattan-bound train. Women in expensive casual wear wheel their carts through the aisles of upscale supermarkets.

HISTORY Most people who live there have no idea an ancient evil lurks behind the facade of well-kept lawns and spacious Colonials. For in 1650, Gideon Winter, a powerful warlock also known as the Dragon, arrived in Hampstead and began a reign of terror.

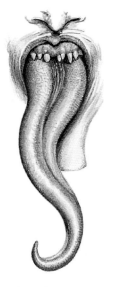

Winter used his powers to take whatever he wanted, including other men's wives. Slain when the townspeople finally rose against him, the Dragon's vengeful spirit has reappeared periodically over the centuries to wreak havoc.

The worst of these manifestations occurred in the late 1970s. It began with a series of murders which quickly escalated into mass hysteria. Children left their beds at night to drown themselves in Long Island Sound. Longtime neighbors became bitter enemies.

Aided by the presence of a toxic chemical spill, Winter nearly destroyed Hampstead. But the Dragon was thwarted by a small group of residents who banded together to save their community.

PHYSICAL CHARACTERISTICS Old records describe Gideon as a dark-eyed, beak-nosed figure who always wore dark clothing. Able to bend others to his will, the Dragon was a frightening, yet somehow charismatic, personage.

Gideon Winter's tongue

In the centuries since Gideon's "death," Winter's shade has appeared in several forms, including those of a satyrlike giant and his namesake dragon. Capable of controlling the living and casting reality-blurring illusions, Gideon's spirit is a deadly supernatural force.

GIDEON WINTER
AKA "THE DRAGON"
SOURCE:
The Floating Dragon
Peter Straub

THE WORLD Almost every culture has its own version of the Frankenstein Myth, in which a powerful sorcerer or brilliant scientist creates a creature too powerful to control, one that eventually turns on him. One of the oldest known variations on this timeless theme is the tale of the Golem.

HISTORY First fashioned on the sun-baked plains of ancient Sumer, Golems are clay or earthen figures brought to life by magical means. During their forced sojourn in Babylon, Hebrew scholars learned how to create these crude automata, and passed this knowledge down from generation to generation. In fact, the term Golem is derived from a biblical Hebrew phrase which translates loosely as a "body without a soul."

The word "truth" becomes "dead" when one letter is removed

The most famous of the Golem legends revolves around Judah Lowe, an eighteenth-century rabbi. Lowe fashioned a Golem to protect the Prague ghetto against pogroms. Unfortunately, as time went on, his creation developed a will of its own, rebelling against the rabbi and forcing him to destroy it.

PHYSICAL CHARACTERISTICS Most Golems are crude, vaguely anthropomorphic creatures, fashioned out of whatever materials are available to their makers. According to Hebrew tradition, Golems are brought to life by inserting a scroll with a sacred word of power in their mouths or by carving a magical phrase on their foreheads. Known for their superhuman strength, they are usually employed as laborers or bodyguards.

GOLEM

SOURCE:
Hebrew Legend

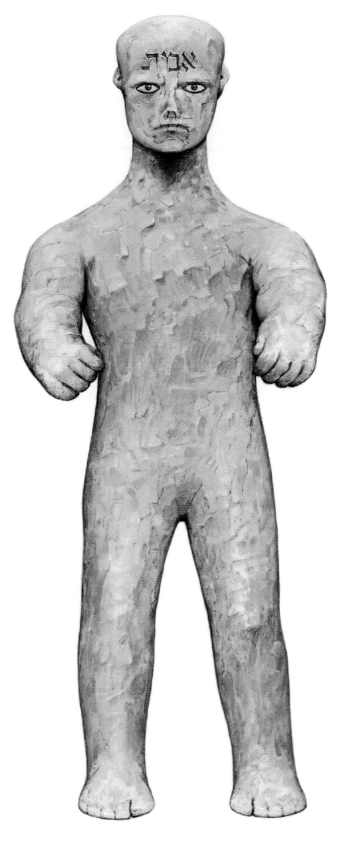

THE WORLD Hidden on a strange alternative Mercury is a marvelous landscape inhabited by manticores and winged hippogriffs. Since time immemorial, two of the humanoid races which inhabit this magical world have been locked in a struggle for planetary dominance.

The Demons, led by Goldry Bluszco, are a noble people who delight in battle. Their ancient foes, the Witches, are feared for their mastery of the black arts.

HISTORY When a messenger arrives at Goldry's court and demands he swear homage to Gorice XI, the tyrannical ruler of Witchland, Bluszco and his brothers, Juss and Spitfire, are outraged. Loath to involve his nation in a protracted war, Goldry offers to resolve the issue through a wrestling match.

If Goldry wins, the Witches will leave the Demons in peace, but if he loses, the Demons must comply with Gorice's demands.

A renowned wrestler who keeps the bones of those he defeats as trophies, Gorice is only too glad to accept.

Meeting on neutral ground at the Castle of the Red Foliot, the two kings engage in single combat. The contest takes an unexpected turn when the Witch is accidentally killed and Goldry emerges victorious.

Brooding in his iron castle in Carcë, Gorice XII, heir to the throne of Witchland, plans a fearsome vengeance. A powerful necromancer, the new king, will use dark sorcery to strike back at Goldry, his family, and Demonland itself.

Peach-ruby ouroboros left-thumb ring

PHYSICAL CHARACTERISTICS Lean and dark-skinned, Gorice XII is known for his piercing green eyes. The king's sharp facial features and clawlike hands have prompted some to compare him to a great bird of prey.

Gorice is wearing a black cobra-skin conjuring mantle dusted with gold and dark mail. His crab-shaped jewel-encrusted crown and matching scepter are ancient symbols of authority.

The most powerful sorcerer on Mercury, Gorice is able to summon deadly creatures from other dimensions and bind them to his will. Skilled in the use of arms, he is a worthy adversary to the valiant Goldry.

Grendel's iron nail

THE WORLD During the eighth century the Danes were among the most feared warriors in Europe. But the reed-infested swamps of their homeland harbored a monster named Grendel, who struck fear into the hearts of these battle-hardened berserkers. Impossible to destroy, he ravaged the countryside, carrying off the mightiest of fighting men like newborn babes.

HISTORY Growing older, Hrothgar, king of the Danes, builds a great hall called Heorot to celebrate his many triumphs. Annoyed by the sounds of merrymaking emanating from the building, the half-human fiend Grendel, who dwells in the wild country nearby, exacts a fearsome revenge.

Every night for the next twelve years Grendel breaks into the building, killing those inside. This rampage continues until the great hero Beowulf learns of Hrothgar's troubles. Sailing from Sweden with a small group of comrades, he arrives at Heorot determined to put an end to the reign of terror.

Grendel's expandable dragonskin glove

PHYSICAL CHARACTERISTICS The son of a water-hag, Grendel is an enormous brute who has rendered himself invulnerable to weapons through some evil magical process. Powerful enough to tear apart enemies with his clawed hands and jaws, Grendel is a murderous fiend who thrives on slaughter. The grisly trophies hanging from his neck are sad reminders of the valiant heroes who tried to slay him.

THE WORLD Feared by the ancient Greeks, the Scythian plains were a wild, gold-rich region near the Black Sea. During the Hellenic era, this huge unexplored expanse of land was home to a unique species called Griffins. When or why they became extinct is unclear, but we have reliable information that these creatures survived well into the first century of the Christian Era.

HISTORY Greek scholars, such as Apollonius of Tyana, claimed Griffins were a strange hybrid of lion and eagle. Modern scientists have speculated that they may have been a mutated form of the beaked dinosaur Protoceratops.

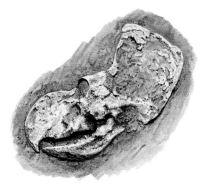

Fossilized skull in matrix

PHYSICAL CHARACTERISTICS Remains found by Scythian nomads indicate Griffins possessed sharp talons and lionlike bodies with long tails. Their frilled skulls rendered them nearly invulnerable to head injury.

Like birds, Griffins reproduced through egg laying. When females were near term they burrowed into the earth, constructing elaborate nests composed of several tunnels. While these excavations often unearthed raw gold from the mineral-rich soil, only the very brave, or very foolish, would risk venturing near a Griffin's nest for the precious metal.

THE WORLD Beyond the gates of sleep lie the dreamlands, a world of strange beauty and dark terror. Somewhere, within their ever-shifting geographies, is Kadath, city of the Great Ones, a place beyond mortal description.

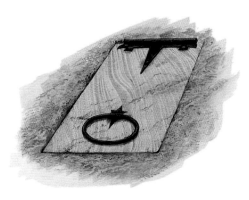

The trapdoor that connects the abyssal caverns with the enchanted wood

HISTORY While humans have visited the dreamlands since the dawn of time, none has ever reached Kadath. One man, Randolph Carter, is determined to be the first.

An intrepid explorer bold enough to befriend the carnivorous Zoogs who inhabit dreamland's forests, Carter is willing to risk his life to get there. Aided by ghoulish and feline allies, he sets out in search of the elusive city. To reach his goal, Randolph must pass through the underground domain of the monstrous Gugs and overcome the traps set for him by Nyarlathotep, the crawling chaos.

PHYSICAL CHARACTERISTICS Former surface dwellers who raised vast stone circles for their sinister rites, the Gugs were condemned to live below by the Great Ones for some unspeakable sin. Among the dreamlands' most horrendous inhabitants, they subsist on the kangaroo-like ghasts, who share their subterranean habitat. But the Gugs will devour anything they can catch.

Huge in stature, the Gugs' enormous taloned paws are attached to their black-furred bodies by surprisingly small forearms. Protected by bony ridges, their pink eyes enable them to stalk prey in almost-complete darkness. The Gugs' mouths open vertically and are equipped with sharp fangs.

Little is known about Gug culture, but they seem to possess a crude form of social organization, which includes a division of labor. Incapable of speech, Gugs communicate with each other through facial expressions.

THE WORLD Light-years from earth, across the dark void of space, lies Witch World, an alien planet where magic works and there is no industry or science as we know it. Witch World is a wild patchwork of walled cities, vast forests, and empty steppes, where daily life is stranger than our wildest dreams.

HISTORY Gillan is a young woman with a mysterious past. An orphan raised in the Keep of Norstead, she has always felt estranged from those around her.

Eager for change, Gillan joins a small group of women pledged as brides to the Were-Riders, mysterious nomads reputed to possess demonic powers. Claimed by a Were-Rider named Herrel, Gillan discovers she is psychic. Her newfound abilities allow her to penetrate the spells of illusion cast by Herrel and learn he is a shape-shifter.

PHYSICAL CHARACTERISTICS Descended from an ancient race with magical skills, the Were-Riders are able to assume animal form at will. Exiled from their home in the Domain of Arvon, they roam Witch World serving as mercenaries.

Herrel's mountain cat form

The Were-Riders' nomadic lifestyle forces them to rely heavily on their horses. Taller and thinner than normal mounts, these horses are highly intelligent and capable of traveling long distances without pause.

The son of an Arvonian father and human mother, Herrel's angular features betray his paternal heritage. His half-breed status makes him the least powerful of the band and an outcast among them.

Were-Riders often shape-shift in battle to frighten their enemies. Herrel's animal form is that of a great mountain cat. The gold totem atop his helmet represents the beast he becomes.

Equipped with a sword, Herrel wears a byrnie of light chain mail. His footwear and breeches are designed to provide comfort and protection while riding.

HERREL

SOURCE:
Year of the Unicorn
Andre Norton

SERIES:
The Witch World Novels

THE WORLD At the dawn of the eleventh century, Christianity had not fully supplanted the ancient religions of the British Isles. Trolls and elves roamed the wildwoods, and the old gods still walked the land. Even the bravest of warriors huddled round their hearth fires after sunset, for fear of what prowled the night.

Troll's heavy stone war-club

HISTORY Seeking a human fosterling who can wield iron, a metal lethal to all magical beings, the elf earl, Imric, kidnaps a Viking chieftain's newborn son. Substituting a changeling spawned by Gora, a captive troll, the earl names the baby Skafloc and raises him as his own.

But Imric has made a deadly mistake. For Gora is kin to Illrede, the troll king. When the changeling, called Valgard by his human parents, reaches manhood he will seek a place at Illrede's side. Angry over years spent as a misfit among humanity, Valgard's desire for revenge ignites a bloody war between elf and troll, a conflict which will cost both sides dearly.

PHYSICAL CHARACTERISTICS Trolls were a fairy tribe native to continental Europe and the British Isles from prehistoric times to the Middle Ages. One of the mightiest of the so-called soulless races, their ongoing struggle with the equally powerful elves eventually reduced them to barbarism.

Hideously ugly to mortal eyes, trolls were known for their green skin, splayed feet, and squat, powerful frames. Communal by nature, they lived together in caves.

Social standing in troll society was determined by prowess in battle, with the greatest warlord serving as king. Female roles were limited to the relatively powerless positions of wife or concubine.

Trolls were not great artisans and produced only primitive weapons and clothing. They did, however, have their own unique form of music, which sounded discordant to human ears.

Perhaps the greatest of their rulers was Illrede, lord of Britain's troll population during the Dark Ages. A great warrior who wore into battle a black helmet and dragonskin coat no blade could pierce, his preferred weapon was a huge ax.

Trollheim, the vast underground city where Illrede held court, was located somewhere far from human habitation, along a rocky shore. Chroniclers describe it as an opulent place, furnished with stolen elfin and human goods.

SOURCE:
The Broken Sword
Poul Anderson

THE WORLD One nation in a world whose wars are fought with sorcery and primitive weapons, Valdemar is an enlightened land surrounded by enemies. To protect their borders and at times their very survival, its rulers have sometimes been forced to hire mercenaries.

HISTORY Raised in a region of small, feuding states, where soldiers of fortune play a key role in settling political disputes, Kerowyn is a strong-willed young woman searching for direction. Ill-suited to the domestic role into which her mother's death has cast her, she would rather ride horses than manage the family estates.

Kerowyn's life changes forever when a band of raiders attacks her brother's wedding feast, murdering her father and abducting the bride. Seeking counsel, Kerowyn turns to her grandmother, Kethry, for help.

A renowned sorceress, Kethry gifts Kerowyn with a magical blade called Need. While it resembles an ordinary sword, Need can only be wielded by a woman and has the power to counteract hostile magic.

Aided by her grandmother's companion, Tarma, Kerowyn tracks down the kidnappers and rescues her brother's fiancée. Her courage impresses Tarma, a former mercenary commander, who agrees to take on Kerowyn as a pupil.

Moving in with Kethry and Tarma, Kerowyn spends the next several years learning the arts of war. Embarking on a career as a professional soldier, she joins the Skybolts, a first-class mercenary company. Kerowyn's skills earn her one promotion after another, eventually placing her in a leadership role.

During the course of her career, Kerowyn will face many challenges. But the greatest of these will be a campaign for Valdemar against an army of religious fanatics led by the prophet Ancar.

Kerowyn's brother's helm

PHYSICAL CHARACTERISTICS Distinguished by her long blond hair and aquamarine eyes, Kerowyn trains regularly to keep herself in shape for combat. Kerowyn's light mail is designed to turn away arrows and blade thrusts, while her overtunic provides protection against the elements.

Known for her riding and archery skills, Kerowyn is a battle-hardened warrior. A brilliant commander, her mastery of military tactics has saved the Skybolts from near disaster on many occasions.

KEROWYN

SOURCE:
By the Sword
Mercedes Lackey

THE WORLD Elm Haven is an unlikely site for an apocalyptic confrontation between the forces of light and darkness. A small Illinois community surrounded by farms, its residents are blissfully unaware of the demonic forces slumbering there.

HISTORY A magical object whose roots date back to ancient Egypt, the Borgia Bell spreads corruption wherever it goes. While the exact nature of the entity dwelling within its metal confines is unknown,

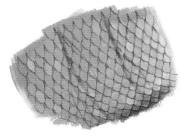

scholars agree it demands human sacrifice. Named after the infamous family of necromancers and assassins who brought it to Rome during the Renaissance, the Bell has the power to control the weak-spirited.

Transported to America by an eccentric millionaire and placed in the steeple of Elm Haven's schoolhouse, the Bell has been biding its time, waiting for the right moment to strike.

Scaled skin with blood vessels visible

When sixth-grader Tubby Cooke vanishes the day before summer vacation, a group of local kids who call themselves the Bike Patrol decides to investigate. The game turns deadly when one of them uncovers the Bell's existence. Stalked by zombies and the deadly Lamprey-worms, the Bike Patrol must find a way to destroy their age-old foe before it eliminates them.

PHYSICAL CHARACTERISTICS Lamprey-worms are named for their long, thick bodies and sucker-equipped mouths. Mindless servants conjured up by the Borgia Bell, they exist solely to eliminate its enemies.

Eyeless and armed with rows of blade-sharp teeth, Lamprey-worms' tough scaled hides and lack of vulnerable organs make them difficult to destroy. Like many creatures of darkness, however, they are vulnerable to holy water.

Powerful burrowers, Lamprey-worms tunnel under their victims and take them by surprise. They are highly efficient killing machines, large enough to swallow a full-grown dog or knock over a truck,

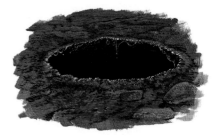

Slime-rimmed aperture of tunnel

LAMPREY-WORMS

SOURCE:
Summer of Night
Dan Simmons

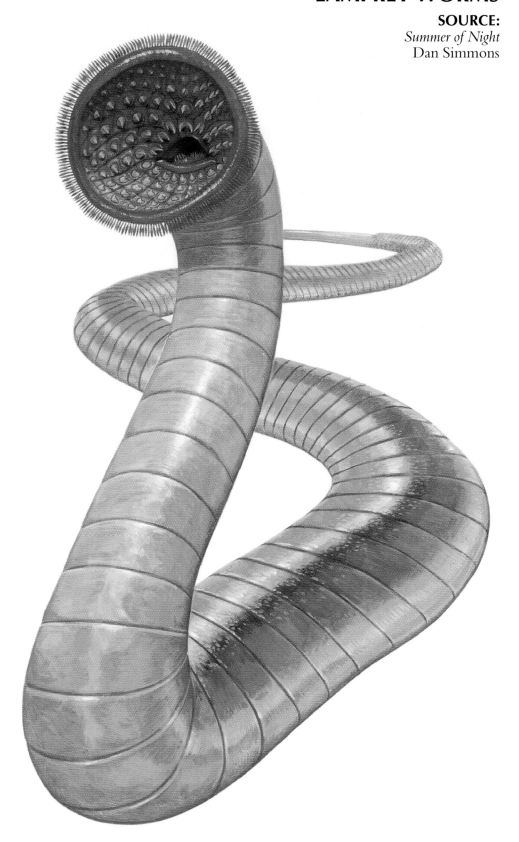

THE WORLD Somewhere beyond the fields we know lies Elfland, a world of ethereal beauty and sensual delight. While many seek Elfland, few manage to cross its enchanted borders.

Ice-crown in early stage of carving

HISTORY Armed with a magical sword forged from thunderbolts by a powerful witch, Prince Alveric sets out in search of this wondrous realm. Succeeding where others have failed, he encounters Lirazel, the king of Elfland's daughter.

Falling in love with Alveric, who is like no one she has ever seen before, Lirazel flees back to earth with the prince. Delighted with the mortal world, the princess marries Alveric and bears him a son.

All is well until Lirazel's father lures her back home. Devastated by the loss of his wife, Alveric vows to reclaim his bride. Setting out on a second quest for Elfland, the prince discovers that it may be impossible to find twice.

PHYSICAL CHARACTERISTICS Said to be the "chiefest glory of Elfland," Lirazel is more beautiful than any earthly woman. Unbound by time, the princess never ages, retaining her youthful appearance over the centuries.

Lirazel's eyes are a strange shade of unearthly blue. She dresses herself in an ornate, floral-patterned robe; her sapphire-colored crown has been sculpted out of blocks of ice.

LIRAZEL

SOURCE:
The King of Elfland's Daughter
Lord Dunsany

THE WORLD Savaged by a nuclear holocaust, the earth has gone through a startling metamorphosis. Once-familiar geographies have been rendered strange. Vastly reduced in numbers, humanity shares the planet with Elves, Trolls, Gnomes, and Dwarfs, mutated or ancient races, who have resurfaced in, or adapted to, this new world.

The Machine-Beast's lethal stinger

HISTORY Raised in the small village of Shady Vale, young Shea Ohmsford, an orphan of human and elfin descent, has led a quiet life. When the Druid historian, Allanon, arrives at Shea's stepfather's inn and tells him he is the last heir of the great Elf-King, Shannara, his first reaction is disbelief.

Shea, explains the Druid, has inherited an awesome responsibility. For only he can fulfill an age-old prophecy by wielding Shannara's sword against the Warlock, Lord Brona, an ancient menace, who has returned to the trouble the world.

Determined to ensure that the magical blade is never used against him, the Warlock dispatches a winged demon, the Skull Bearer, to destroy Shea. Escaping into the wilderness with his foster brother Flick, Shea realizes he's become a key player in a deadly game. But to reach safety, the Ohmsfords must traverse a landscape filled with dangerous creatures, like the Machine-Beast.

PHYSICAL CHARACTERISTICS A survivor of the ancient wars which destroyed much of the world, the Machine-Beast is a partially mechanical life-form that has taken drastic steps to adapt to its environment. Preying on whatever it can catch, it hides in the ruins of an abandoned city, waiting for victims.

Insectlike in nature, the Machine-Beast has grafted metal sheets over portions of its body, in an effort to repair its decaying frame. What little remains of its original flesh is covered with coarse black hair.

The tentacles above the Machine-Beast's eyes are tipped with toxic stingers, whose touch can be lethal. Equipped with multiple legs, it is able to move quickly when fleeing or stalking food.

Incorporation of metal plate's into the creature's skin

MACHINE-BEAST

SOURCE:
The Sword of Shannara
Terry Brooks

SERIES:
The Shannara Novels

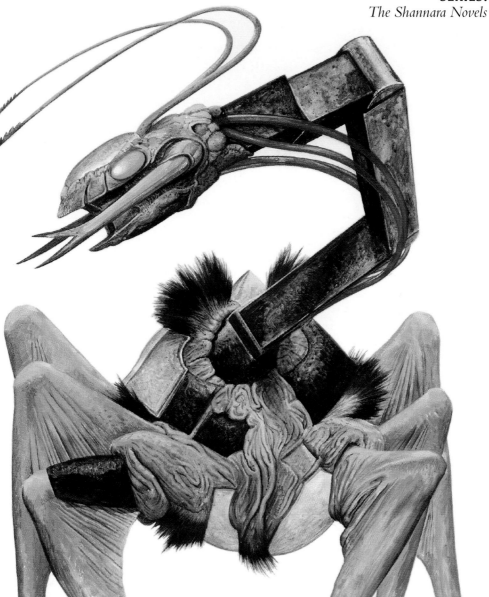

THE WORLD Long ago, in a lost age between the fall of Rome and the Middle Ages, a great king ruled Britain. Known as Arthur Pendragon, his legend haunts us to this day. To understand fully this charismatic leader who united a fragmented nation under his banner, we must examine the role Arthur's half sister, Morgaine, played in shaping his destiny.

HISTORY The daughter of Arthur's mother, Igraine, and her first husband, Duke Gorlois of Cornwall, Morgaine was a precocious child. Sometimes called Morgaine of the Fairies, because of her small, dark appearance, it was rumored that the blood of the little people, who were the land's original inhabitants, flowed in her veins.

Sensing her potential, Morgaine's aunt, Viviane, took her to Avalon. A hidden isle sacred to Britain's ancient matriarchal religion, it was the place where the mysteries of the Mother Goddess were studied.

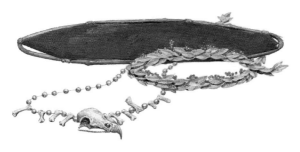

Ritual drum, garland, and necklace

Under her aunt's tutelage Morgaine learned to utilize the "sight," a limited precognitive ability shared by the women in her family. She was also taught to cast glamours, spells of illusion which altered how others perceived her.

In time, Morgaine attained the rank of priestess. A skilled healer, musician, and seamstress, she was a woman of many talents.

Passionately devoted to her faith, Morgaine was determined to defend it against the intolerant Christianity championed by Gwenhwyfar, Arthur's Christian Queen. This conflict, between the two women he loved most, placed the King in an impossible position and eventually brought about his downfall.

PHYSICAL CHARACTERISTICS Painted with astrological signs and bearing the crescent mark of Avalon upon her forehead, Morgaine has been prepared for the holy rite of King Making. This ritual, where she lay with Arthur prior to his coronation and symbolically bound him to the land, had disastrous consequences.

Morgaine became pregnant and gave birth to a son, who came to be known as Mordred. The child proved to be his father's nemesis, destroying all Arthur had built.

MORGAINE

SOURCE:
The Mists of Avalon
Marion Zimmer Bradley

THE WORLD Perhaps the most unusual celestial body in the universe, Discworld is a flat planet supported by four great elephants, perched atop the shell of the giant star turtle Great A'Tuin. Anything can and does happen on this cosmic anomaly, where even the Grim Reaper has a sense of humor.

HISTORY Death is stressed out. Who wouldn't be after a few thousand years without a night off? Traveling to an employment fair in search of an apprentice, the Grim Reaper selects a naive country boy named Mort and decides to teach him the tricks of the trade.

Mort has mixed feelings about the job. It has some interesting fringe benefits, like learning to walk through walls. He gets to wear great clothes and use Death's scythe. On the downside, he has to put up with his master's adopted daughter, Ysabell, who has developed a crush on him.

Things go fairly well until Mort takes matters into his own hands, sparing a beautiful princess and claiming her assassin instead. His boss is understandably enraged when this small bit of personal initiative alters the course of history. Mort is now about to discover that annoying the Grim Reaper is definitely a bad career move.

One of Death's hourglasses

PHYSICAL CHARACTERISTICS

Originally a tall, clumsy, red-haired, youth, Mort undergoes significant changes in his appearance as a result of his association with Death. Going from nerdy to sinister, his brown eyes acquire a strange blue glow.

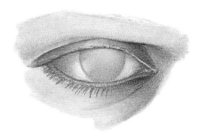

Clad in his master's black cloak, Mort bears Death's scythe. Used to sever the thread which binds souls to their bodies, **Mort's fully transformed eye**

the blade of this device is so finely honed as to be transparent.

MORT

SOURCE:
Mort
Terry Pratchett

SERIES:
The Discworld Novels

THE WORLD Deverry is an ancient kingdom bordered by sea and high mountains. While its social structure is slightly similar to Medieval Europe's, Deverry's history is very different. For untold ages wandering sages have practiced a magical art form called dweomer, a secret body of knowledge that has been passed down from master to student.

HISTORY Born a prince of Deverry, Nevyn was determined to give up his privileged position and study dweomer. Unfortunately, a king's son, even one who is not directly in line for the throne, has responsibilities, and Nevyn's father refused to grant him leave.

Determined to go his own way, Nevyn slipped out of the palace to seek out the dweomer master Rhegor. His actions set in motion a sequence of events which caused the death of his beloved Brangwen and two others.

Heartbroken, Nevyn swore to make amends no matter how long it took. Beyond the bounds of time and space, the Great Ones, who rule all creation, heard his vow and granted him immortality, so he could track the trio of souls through their various incarnations and atone for his mistakes.

In centuries of wandering through Deverry and the elfin lands beyond, Nevyn has never succeeded in achieving his goal. But when he encounters Cullyn, a battle-hardened mercenary, and his young daughter Jill, the prince's luck begins to change.

Nevyn's silver spade

PHYSICAL CHARACTERISTICS Disguised as a traveling herbalist, the four-hundred-year-old Nevyn wears the body and simple attire of an elderly peasant. The greatest living master of dweomer, Nevyn is able to converse with the Wildfolk, fairylike creatures invisible to most humans, and project his astral form into other dimensions. A skilled healer, he is sought out by rich and poor alike.

Nevyn's travels have taken him into regions inhabited by the elfin peoples, and he has learned something of their culture and crafts. As the prince has discovered, the elves possess their own form of magic, which includes the ability to shape-shift.

NEVYN

SOURCE:
Daggerspell
Katharine Kerr

SERIES:
The Deverry Novels

THE WORLD The earth is dying. An ailing sun illuminates a tortured landscape, where powerful mages tamper with natural laws. Demons from the Overworld, an alternate universe bordering on our own, prey on those foolish enough to summon them.

Once-great cities have become wastelands inhabited by bizarre creatures. Human survivors wake each morning wondering when the long night will arrive.

Nissifer's retracting stinger

HISTORY Cugel the Clever, an amoral rogue who lives by his wits, is banished to the empty shores of Shanglestone Strand by the Laughing Magician, Iuconnu. Vowing revenge, he works his way back toward his enemy's home in Almery.

During the course of his adventures Cugel acquires a demon scale called Spatterlight. This powerful magical relic, which absorbs organic matter through one of its sides, will help him survive the rigors of his journey.

PHYSICAL CHARACTERISTICS A strange insectlike monster, Nissifer passes for human by concealing her alien frame under hat, veil, and loose-fitting clothes. While little is known about the origins or habits of her kind, they are most likely one of the mutated species common to the far future "Dying Earth."

Hunting by night, Nissifer devours her victims, leaving only the bones. Her primary weapon is a retractable stinger, whose touch causes convulsions and death. Capable of emitting noxious fumes when threatened, she is a foe to be reckoned with.

Cugel and Nissifer cross paths on a caravan journey. When Cugel discovers her preying on fellow travelers, Nissifer attacks him, only to be destroyed by Spatterlight.

NISSIFER

SOURCE:
Cugel's Saga
Jack Vance

SERIES:
The Dying Earth Novels

THE WORLD In a bygone era, when dinosaurs roamed the earth, the beaches of what is now England were home to a race of magical beings called Psammeads. While many perished during the climatic upheavals and geological shifts which ended the Age of Reptiles, others burrowed underground and went into a trancelike sleep, only to be dug up and awakened by unwary humans.

HISTORY While on a family outing to Kent, a group of children playing in a gravel pit accidentally unearth a Psammead. To their surprise, the creature, which speaks perfect English, explains it has the power to grant wishes. But there's a catch. Whatever they ask for will vanish after sunset, so they must think carefully before making a request.

The Psammead warns them that getting what they ask for may have unexpected consequences, but the children do not heed its advice. On one occasion, they ask for gold and receive strange coins no merchant will take. A demand for wings so they can fly like birds results in their being stranded atop a church roof at the end of the day. After several of these misadventures, the children finally realize that magic is not something to be tampered with.

Psammead eyes retracted

PHYSICAL CHARACTERISTICS Psammeads, or sand-fairies, are small, fat, furry creatures with long monkeylike arms and legs, and batlike ears. They are also known for their strange eye stalks, which can be extended or retracted at will.

Even though they once inhabited the beaches in great numbers, Psammeads can not abide the touch of water, which makes them ill. In later years this prompted them to take up residence in dryer locales, like sand and gravel pits.

Sand-fairies live underground and use their hands for burrowing. Cantankerous by nature, they enjoy lecturing those they encounter.

Psammeads swell up like balloons when using their powers to grant wishes. While they are able to provide things for others, sand-fairies' magical abilities do not allow them to grant their own requests.

PSAMMEAD

SOURCE:
Five Children and It
E. Nesbit

THE WORLD The Realm of Sky, is a world of floating continents separated by an ocean of air. Humans, dwarfs, and elves struggle to survive in this hostile environment, where water is more precious than gold.

There are only two means of travel between the Realm's isolated landmasses, the domesticated winged dragons favored by humans, or the magical flying ships utilized by elves. Neither is foolproof, and many an unwary traveler has been lost to the void.

HISTORY Spared from the headsman's block by King Stephen, the Realm's most powerful human lord, Hugh the Hand knows he has incurred a debt that must be repaid. But Hugh is shocked when Stephen orders him to assassinate his young son, Bane. As time goes on, Hugh learns there's more to Bane than is readily apparent, and his father may have good reasons for wanting him dead.

PHYSICAL CHARACTERISTICS The Realm of Sky is home to four different kinds of dragons. While they serve different purposes, each must be domesticated by skilled handlers before being put to work.

The so-called Battle Dragons are the largest variety and are used to transport troops and cargo from place to place.

Their more compact cousins, the Dragon Steeds, are ridden by soldiers known as Dragon Knights. Trained for combat, the Dragon Steeds fight alongside their masters in battle.

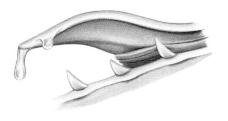

Acid-dripping tongue

Courier Dragons are the smallest of the four breeds. Known for their speed, they are favored by messengers, who need to relay vital information quickly.

Wingless, yet capable of flight through some unknown means, Quicksilver Dragons are used as mounts by powerful wizards. More intelligent than any other type of dragon, they are mean-natured and can only be mastered by magic.

Red-eyed and sinuous, Quicksilvers curl their bodies into snakelike coils when nervous. They do not breathe fire, but secrete a flesh-searing acid from their fanged mouths when provoked.

QUICKSILVER DRAGON

SOURCE:
Dragon Wing
Margaret Weis & Tracy Hickman

SERIES:
The Death Gate Cycle

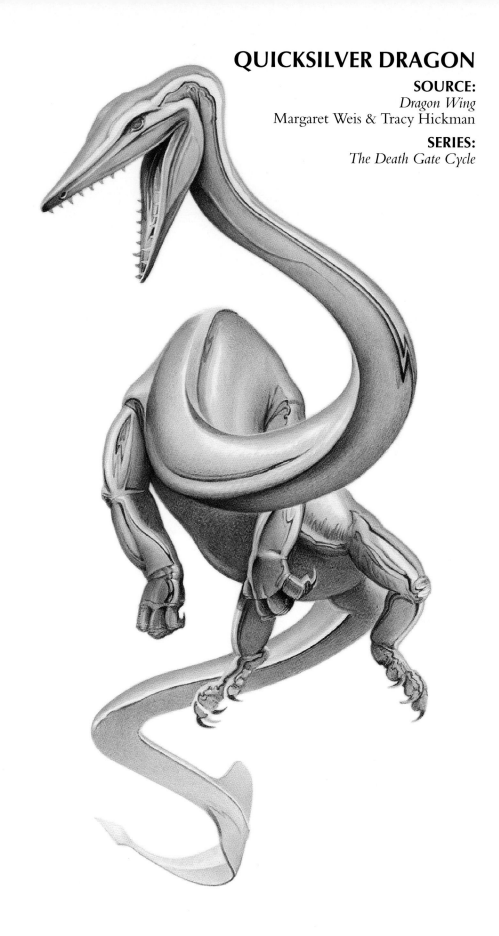

THE WORLD During the early years of the Renaissance, a terrible plague swept through Europe. Labeled the Red Death, its symptoms included mind-numbing pain, vertigo, and uncontrollable bleeding. All those who contracted this dread disease died in terrible agony, shunned by those around them, who feared its rapid spread.

HISTORY Only the mad and the desperate dream of cheating Death, and Prince Prospero possessed both those qualities. When the Red Death broke out among his peasants, the prince secluded his court in a fortified abbey.

A bizarre place that reflected Prospero's twisted aesthetic sense, the sanctuary contained a suite of different-colored rooms and a great ebony clock. For six months the prince and his court feasted behind stone walls while the Red Death ravaged the countryside. Then, finally believing themselves secure, the aristocrats threw a masque, a gala crashed by an unwelcome guest.

The Mask of the Red Death

PHYSICAL CHARACTERISTICS Appearing as a blood-splattered corpse clad in grave clothes, Death visited Prospero's ball in the guise of the pestilence decimating his lands. Striking down the highborn foolish enough to think they could escape him, the Grim Reaper proved he plays no favorites.

THE WORLD Everyone knows the story of Dorothy who came to Oz on the wings of a tornado and found her way back to Kansas after many amazing adventures. However, the tale doesn't end there.

Just after Dorothy's departure, her friend the Scarecrow was made King of the Emerald City, while Nick Chopper, the Tin Woodman, went on to become Emperor of the Winkies. As Dorothy's faithful companions soon discovered, being in charge is a lot more difficult than it looks.

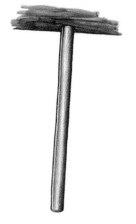

Saw-Horse's leg after Ozma's gilding

HISTORY Brought up in the country of the Gillikins, somewhere in the northern reaches of Oz, Tip has no memory of his parents. Like most young boys, Tip is a mischievous child who enjoys playing tricks on Mombi, the old crone who has raised him.

A would-be witch who secretly practices the black arts, the woman's sour disposition rubs Tip the wrong way.

Returning home from a trip to visit a local wizard, Mombi discovers Tip has constructed a pumpkin-headed effigy and placed it in the road to scare her. Angry at the boy, Mombi's first impulse is to tear the thing apart, but she decides to try her newly acquired Powder of Life, on it instead. The Powder animates the figure, giving Tip's construct a life of its own.

The old woman vows to turn Tip into a statue for the jest. Having no desire to become a permanent fixture in Mombi's garden, Tip flees, taking the Powder of Life and his creation, whom he christens Jack Pumpkinhead, with him.

En route to the Emerald City to seek counsel from the Scarecrow, Tip and Jack encounter a wooden saw-horse. Jack utilizes the Powder to bring the object to life for use as a means of transportation. Unaccustomed to being alive, the Saw-Horse proves to be a stubborn creature with an iron will.

PHYSICAL CHARACTERISTICS A wooden construct brought to life by magical means, the Saw-Horse has two knots for eyes, a stake protruding from its back, and a branchlike tail. The Saw-Horse's long ears were carved out of bark and added on by Tip, so that it would be able to hear his commands.

Able to travel great distances at a rapid pace without tiring, the Saw-Horse is a reliable, if somewhat temperamental, steed. Graced with a strong personality, the Saw-Horse has a tendency to bicker with Jack Pumpkinhead.

SAW-HORSE

SOURCE:
The Land of Oz
L. Frank Baum

SERIES:
The Wonderful Oz Books

THE WORLD Earthsea is a world of vast oceans where magic is ever-present and technology is limited to wind and muscle power. The planet's human inhabitants live on a series of islands, where they scratch out a living as mariners, craftspeople, or fisherfolk.

Those who display an aptitude for sorcery are sent to study at the Wizard's Academy on the Island of Roke. Trained by masters, they are taught the magical arts and that power must be used responsibly.

Graduates of the Academy perform a variety of tasks, including healing and weather working. They also protect the population from dangerous beasts, like the dragons who sometimes take up residence near inhabited areas.

A humanoid form of the shadow

HISTORY Perhaps the greatest mage in Earthsea's history was Ged, who later took the name of Sparrowhawk. Born on the rocky isle of Gont, Ged exhibited a talent for magic at an early age.

Apprenticed to a local wizard called Ogion, his thirst for knowledge eventually led him to Roke. Ged was an impulsive student who allowed his classmates to goad him into acting foolishly.

Determined to prove his skills, he tried to summon a dead woman's spirit. The attempt backfired, releasing a shadow-beast from the twilight realm between life and death.

Temporarily banished by a teacher's sacrifice, it returned to stalk Ged. To survive, the young wizard was forced to conquer his fear and confront the monster his misuse of power had unleashed.

PHYSICAL CHARACTERISTICS Although lacking true substance, the shadow-beast is able to assume many different forms, including a bear-like shape, the semblances of several of Ged's friends, and a doppelgänger of the young wizard. It also has the power to seize control of people and transform them into gebbeths, mindless puppets subject to its will.

Unaffected by gravity, the shadow-beast can drift through the air and walk on water. A silent, ghostly presence, it is truly nightmarish.

SHADOW

SOURCE:
A Wizard of Earthsea
Ursula K. Le Guin

SERIES:
The Earthsea Novels

THE WORLD Tormance is distant planet circling the star Arcturus. A world of savage beauty, it is ruled by the enigmatic deity, Surtur.

HISTORY Bored with life in England, Maskull, a man undergoing a spiritual crisis, yearns to discover the meaning of life. Introduced to a mysterious stranger called Krag at a séance, Maskull falls under his spell.

Krag offers to send Maskull to Tormance. While he doubts Krag will be able to make good on his promise, Maskull agrees to meet him at a deserted observatory in the Scottish highlands. Placed inside a torpedo-like vehicle, Maskull is transported through space to his destination.

Lateral view showing sucker mouth

Awakening on Tormance, Maskull discovers he has grown a tentacle-like third limb, knobs on both sides of his neck, and on his forehead an extra organ, known as a breve, which allows him to communicate telepathically. Aided by Joiwind, a beautiful native, who possesses the same physical structures, he sets out in search of Surtur.

Along the way Maskull encounters Oceaxe, a strange female able to summon flying monsters called shrowks. Oceaxe takes Maskull for a ride on one of these strange creatures, allowing him to study the alien landscape of Tormance from the air.

PHYSICAL CHARACTERISTICS Huge fliers native to Tormance, shrowks propel themselves through the air by employing their leg fins. Surviving on blood, shrowks paralyze prey through hypnosis, then stab it to death with their rostral spike. Like terrestrial leeches, they feed by draining their victims' vital fluids through sucker-equipped mouths.

The typical shrowk has slippery reptilian skin and a long neck, covered by a hairy black mane. Strong, but not particularly intelligent, they can be coerced into providing transport by the telepathic humanoids native to the planet.

SHROWK

SOURCE:
A Voyage to Arcturus
David Lindsay

THE WORLD Hidden beneath the rocky shores of a remote Pacific island, lies a lost civilization older than the great pyramids of Egypt. Populated by demigods and strange froglike humanoids, it is home to a technology vastly superior to our own.

HISTORY When an urgent appeal from a friend brings Dr. Walter Goodwin, an American botanist, to the small atoll of Nan-Tauach, he has no idea what to expect. Stumbling across a hidden portal, Goodwin and his companions find themselves transported to a subterranean realm.

This realm is governed by a sinister priesthood centered around the Shining One, a strange creature that derives energy from moonlight. Its rulers are preparing an assault on the outside world. Fortunately for humanity, these evil theocrats are opposed by the Silent Ones, a triad of immortal beings with almost-godlike powers.

Close-up of eye showing fiery glints

Silent Ones' finely scaled hand

PHYSICAL CHARACTERISTICS The Silent Ones are ancient entities who have dwelt in their underground domain for countless aeons. Masters of a superscience so advanced it appears magical, they created the Shining One, but have long since lost control of it.

The last survivors of a race whose existence predates Homo sapiens, the trio, consisting of one female and two males, is all that remains of a once-great empire.

Silent Ones' distinguishing features include visored foreheads, black pupilless eyes, beaked noses, and six-fingered hands. It is difficult for the casual observer to tell the difference between the males and females of the species. Silent Ones often appear cloaked in a golden mist, which may be some type of energy field.

Benevolent in nature, the Silent Ones favor reason over violence. Careful students of human behavior, they have long kept a keen eye on the surface world from their secret lair.

THE WORLD The ruins of an old mansion in a desolate region of Ireland harbor a dark secret. Surrounded by woods, the house was once a gateway through time and space to alien realms.

Those who linger in the area are plagued with strange dreams of a great arena populated by terrifying forms, including a huge swinelike monstrosity. As their spirits wander through the fields of sleep, they may even catch glimpses of cosmic catastrophes which foreshadow the end of the universe.

HISTORY Just before the Great War, two vacationers stumbled on the ruins and found a journal left behind by the mansion's final occupant. This alarming document provides a first-person account of the author's struggle against the murderous Swine-things. While the exact nature of their connection with the house is not understood, the Swine-things appear to have been obsessed with it.

PHYSICAL CHARACTERISTICS Swine- things are evil piglike humanoids who combine the worst attributes of man and animal. Little is known about their history or culture, but it is assumed they are underground dwellers, explaining the unhealthy, luminous green tinge of their skin.

Often seen traveling in packs, Swine-things are capable of acting in consort. They communicate through a rudimentary language that sounds like grunting to human ears.

Although bipedal, Swine-things run on all fours when stalking prey. While their facial structure bears some resemblance to a human's, their snouts, small eyes, and oddly shaped ears are distinctly porcine. Naturally aggressive, they attack without provocation and have been observed cannibalizing their own dead.

Swine-Thing's clawed paw

82

THE WORLD For as long as human memory, the mist-shrouded peaks of Japan have been home to the Tengu, mountain goblins with an unusual sense of humor. While no one is sure where these creatures came from, it is believed they migrated across the cold seas from the Chinese mainland before the words of the Buddha reached Nippon.

HISTORY Ancient Japanese writings describe the Tengu as malicious creatures who delight in causing mayhem. Accounts of Tengu spiriting away children, who would later be found wandering aimlessly in a disoriented state, are commonplace.

Tengu were said to derive particular pleasure from tormenting the Buddhist priests who came to the mountains to study them. Their tricks included lighting fires in front of temples and leading the unfortunate holy men astray in isolated areas.

Fond of meddling in human affairs, Tengu often interfered in political disputes. The great twelfth-century warrior, Yoshitsune, was reputed to have a Tengu teacher, who instructed him in martial arts and military tactics. These lessons enabled the famed warlord to win a decisive victory over his enemies.

PHYSICAL CHARACTERISTICS Tengu are said to be able to change form at will. They often appear as strange figures with long bizarre noses, and sometimes disguise themselves as priests or nuns, to fool those who encounter them.

Humanoid form of Tengu

Perhaps the most unusual of the many varieties of Tengu are the karasu. Combining human and crow-like characteristics, karasu are frequently seen carrying ring-tipped staffs known as shakujos. These tools provide their owners with protection against enchantments and are useful in exorcising demons. On a more down-to-earth level, shakujos can also be used in combat to tangle and snap spear blades. The strangely shaped cap, or tokin, worn by the karasu, doubles as a drinking cup.

Tengu were fiercely protective of their territory and sternly punished those who entered areas under their control. Sometimes identified with the vengeful spirits of the dead, many chroniclers believed they could take possession of people and use them as mouthpieces.

Over time, the peasants who lived in mountain villages learned to coexist with the Tengu. To this day, many still leave offerings of rice and bean paste outside their doors, to appease their supernatural neighbors.

THE WORLD Just over the hills and through the Wild Wood, lies a river whose waters run cool and clear. Along its quiet banks lives a group of animals, the curious Mole, the stalwart Rat, the valiant Badger, and the clever Toad, whose world bears a striking resemblance to Edwardian England.

HISTORY The sole occupant of Toad Hall, the grandest residence on the river, Mr. Toad is an animal given to extremes. When Toad develops a passion for motorcars his friends, Rat, Mole, and Badger, sense it will lead to trouble.

Mr. Toad's hair

Ignoring his comrades' advice, Toad begins squandering his fortune on a succession of flashy automobiles. Disaster strikes when Toad "borrows" a car without asking and is thrown in jail for the theft.

Aided by the jailer's daughter, Toad disguises himself as a washerwoman and escapes. Surviving by his wits, Toad works his way back to the river, only to discover that his home has been taken over by Weasels and Stoats from the Wild Wood.

PHYSICAL CHARACTERISTICS Like most animals living along the river, Toad possesses human attributes, such as hair and the ability to walk upon two legs. A bit of a dandy, he has a taste for expensive clothes and favors fine suits with waistcoats.

Snobbish by nature, Toad has a tendency to talk a great deal without listening to others. Used to having his own way, he swells up to several times his normal size when angry or frustrated.

MR. TOAD

SOURCE:
The Wind in the Willows
Kenneth Grahame

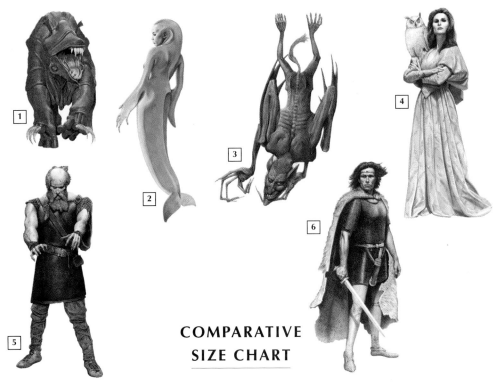

COMPARATIVE
SIZE CHART

	KEY	SIZE		KEY	SIZE
1	Alzabo	4"	26	Kerowyn	5'10"
2	Anyanwu	5'6"	27	Lamprey Worms	6'
3	Baital	5'6"	28	Lirazel	5'5"
4	Beatritz de Barbentain	6'	29	Machine Beast	30'
5	Biargram Ironhand	6'	30	Morgaine	5'2"
6	Bran Mak Morn	5'8"	31	Mort	6'2"
7	Camber	5'6"	32	Nevyn	5'6"
8	Caterpillar	2½"	33	Nissifer	5'6"
9	Changeling	4'	34	Psammead	3'2"
10	Chuz	6'	35	Quicksilver Dragon	10'1"
11	Corum	6'5"	36	Red Death	6'2"
12	Dara	15'	37	Saw Horse	4'
13	Dark One	10'	38	Shadow	6'1"
14	Drool Rockworm	6'	39	Shrowk	10'
15	Eastern Afrit	6'	40	Silent One	15'
16	Elemental	5'6"	41	Swine-Thing	5'3"
17	Gek-A-Gek	3'	42	Tengu	5'6"
18	Gideon Winter	5'6"	43	Mr. Toad	5'
19	Golem	7'6"	44	Toothguard	2'
20	Gorice	7'	45	Trolloc	8'
21	Grendel	14'	46	Unicorn	6'
22	Griffin	3'	47	Unseelie Court Assassins	5'6"
23	Gugs	20'	48	Vodyanoi	8'
24	Herrel	6'	49	White Lady	6'
25	Illrede	5'	50	Wolfen	3'

THE WORLD Those who share their lives with cats realize that cats are intelligent creatures with minds of their own. What we don't know is that they possess a secret language and culture, hidden from our eyes since the dawn of time.

Late at night, while humans slumber, our feline friends gather in open fields and back alleys to swap stories of the old days before two-legged folk came into the world.

HISTORY Fritti Tailchaser is a young cat struggling to survive on his own. When his friend Hushpad and several other local felines mysteriously disappear, Fritti embarks on a quest to discover what has befallen them.

Accompanied by a kitten called Pouncequick, and Eatbugs, an elderly cat with a secret past, Fritti sets out on a long journey. The trio's adventures will take them to Firsthome, where the Queen of Cats holds court, through a perilous forest, and into the clutches of the demonic Hearteater.

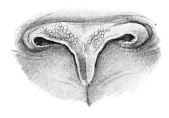

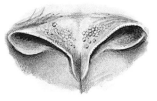

Toothguard's dilating nostrils

PHYSICAL CHARACTERISTICS Toothguards are vile beasts who guard Vastnir, Hearteater's underground lair. Furless and blind, they have fanged muzzles containing rows of needlelike teeth.

Although capable of conversing in standard feline speech, Toothguards have difficulty expressing themselves, often slurring their words. Their sharp sense of hearing enables them to find their way around without the benefit of eyesight. Crafty and manipulative, Toothguards enjoy conspiring against Hearteater's other minions, the Claws and Boneguards.

TOOTHGUARD

SOURCE:
Tailchaser's Song
Tad Williams

THE WORLD In an ancient place, where age after age has spun by on the Wheel of Time, an unending struggle between the forces of light and darkness is being played out. Fought with the awesome powers of the True Source, wild supernatural energies only a select few can control, the conflict has drained oceans and leveled mountains.

An avian form of Trolloc

HISTORY Brought up by his father on a farm near the small community of Two Rivers, Rand hasn't seen much of the outside world. Still, something about the hooded rider he spies en route to the town's annual Bel Tine festival sets his nerves on edge.

Rand's instincts are correct, for the stranger is an agent of the Dark One, a supernatural creature who is evil incarnate. Free after centuries of imprisonment, the Dark One has dispatched servants to capture Rand and his friends. Convinced one of them is a reincarnation of known as the Dragon, the Dark One is determined to destroy his old enemy, no matter what the cost.

PHYSICAL CHARACTERISTICS Half-human, half-animal, Trollocs are the shock troops of the Dark One's armies. Created through genetic engineering, they are ferocious fighters who delight in death and destruction.

Trollocs' fingered hands allow them to utilize weapons, such as the curved scythe-type swords they are often issued. Frequently clad in black mail, spiked at the wrist and elbows, and leather trousers, only the most skilled of warriors can best one in single combat.

Not great thinkers, Trollocs possess a certain animal cunning. Although capable of speech, their nonhuman vocal cords make them difficult to understand.

Trolloc units are supervised by officers called Myrddraals. Also known as Halfmen or Fades, they are masters of the black arts who rule through terror and demand complete obedience.

The Trolloc social order is divided into thirteen tribal groupings, which include the Ahf'frait, Al'ghol, Bhan'sheen, Dha'vol, Dhai'mon, Dhjin'nen, Ghar'ghael, Ghob'hlin, Gho'hlem, Ghraem'lan, Ko'bal, and Kno'mon bands. Universally feared, they are one of the most potent weapons in the Dark One's arsenal.

Enameled badges of the
1. Dha'vol—Horned Skull
2. Dhai'mon—Iron Fist
3. Ahf'frait—Whirlwind

Main illustration depicts a Trolloc of the Ko'bal Band—Trident Badge

TROLLOC

SOURCE:
The Eye of the World
Robert Jordan

SERIES:
The Wheel of Time

THE WORLD Somewhere in a land of great castles and noble princes, there lies an enchanted grove. For as long as anyone can remember, this place has been home to a noble Unicorn, who may be the last of her kind.

HISTORY Curious about life beyond the lilac wood where she's dwelt for ages, the Unicorn ventures into the outside world and discovers that

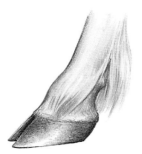

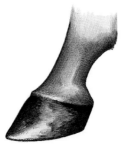

her kin have vanished. Setting out in search of them, she is imprisoned by Mommy Fortuna, an evil witch, and exhibited in a carnival.

Freed by Schmendrick, a magician with a confidence problem, the Unicorn and her liberator resume the quest. During the course of their travels they are joined by a young woman named Molly Grue.

The trio's odyssey takes them to the joyless domain of King Haggard. While the answers the Unicorn seeks are hidden there, to get them she will have to do battle with the fearsome Red Bull.

PHYSICAL CHARACTERISTICS A mature representative of her species, the Unicorn is snow-white in color. Slender-necked, with cloven hoofs, thin legs, and a tail resembling a lion's, she is among the most graceful of living creatures. More than mere ornamentation, her horn is a deadly weapon, which also possesses magical healing powers.

Solitary by nature, Unicorns are territorial beasts who pick a single spot and remain there for long periods of time. Immortal and vain, their preferred habitats are wooded areas with clear pools that allow them to study their reflections.

A comparison between a unicorn's hoof and a horse's hoof

SOURCE:
The Last Unicorn
Peter S. Beagle

THE WORLD A vicious turf war is being fought on the streets of contemporary Minneapolis. Only this time the players are not rival gangs, but two fey tribes, the Seelie and Unseelie courts, who are determined to destroy one another. Invisible to mortal eyes, these ancient antagonists will play out their blood feud in the parks and back alleys of the city.

HISTORY Eddi McCandry is a musician trying to survive on the Minneapolis club scene. Walking home late one night through empty windswept streets, she finds herself stalked by a huge black dog.

Assassin's long knife

Knocked unconscious, Eddi reawakens and discovers that her pursuer is a phouka, a fairy creature able to assume canine form at will. McCandry listens in horror as the phouka explains that her presence is required by the Seelie Court. Pressed into service as a sort of mascot, it seems her appearance on the field of honor will ensure that the wounds suffered by the normally immortal fey combatants will be fatal ones.

All Eddi wants to do is escape. But she soon learns that flight is not an option. For without the phouka's protection she will be hunted down by hideous members of the Unseelie Court. Trapped in a situation stranger than her wildest dreams, McCandry is about to embark on a terror-filled odyssey which will change her world forever.

PHYSICAL CHARACTERISTICS Grey-skinned, with cloudy white eyes, snoutlike noses, and sharp teeth, the Unseelie Court Assassins are horrific to behold. Merciless killers who silently stalk their prey, they are armed with translucent bows and long knives.

Like all Unseelie fey, the Assassins are creatures of darkness and enjoy inspiring terror in mortals. Enraged over their lower social status in the realm of faerie, they harbor great bitterness toward the Seelie Court.

UNSEELIE COURT ASSASSINS

SOURCE:
The War for the Oaks
Emma Bull

THE WORLD During the Middle Ages most of Russia was wilderness. Great cities, like Kiev and Moscow, were isolated from one another by endless miles of steppe and forest. These vast regions were home to strange creatures and powerful wizards who preyed on wayfarers.

HISTORY Accused of a murder he did not commit, Pyetr Kochevikov flees the town of Vojvoda with his friend Sasha Misurov. Traveling through an isolated area, they stumble on the hut of the wizard Uulamets.

In return for his hospitality, Uulamets enlists their aid in tracking down the spirit of his daughter, Eveshka. Slain by a River-thing or Vodyanoi, she has returned as a Rusalka, a ghost who survives by preying on the living. If left unchecked, she will grow stronger and stronger, draining the life force from the surrounding forest.

Uulamets is convinced he can resurrect Eveshka, but to accomplish this he must trap the Vodyanoi. Without realizing it, Pyetr and Sasha find themselves ensnared in the wizard's obsessive plan to capture the River-thing.

PHYSICAL CHARACTERISTICS Serpentine in nature, Vodyanois are aquatic creatures who inhabit the rivers of Eastern Europe. Intelligent and capable of speech, they are able to change size and shape at will.

Vodyanoi's bone collection

Hostile to humans, River-things often disguise themselves as old men to lure the unwary near. Luckless travelers who blunder into their clutches are dragged into the water and drowned. They are fond of bones and keep hordes of their victims' remains near their dwelling places.

Vodyanois can travel across land but are strongest within their natural element of water. Direct sunlight and salt are harmful to River-things, who take great care to avoid them.

Inclined toward treachery, Vodyanois can be made to do the bidding of wizards powerful enough to learn their true names. Even then, they are not to be trusted and frequently twist information to suit their own purposes.

SOURCE:
Rusalka
C. J. Cherryh

THE WORLD The secluded foothills of the Adirondack Mountains harbor a dark secret. For generations, this isolated region has been home to a race of strange creatures. While most of their kind only wish to be left alone, some can be murderously dangerous.

HISTORY Tired of life in the fast lane, Phil Hastings, a successful screenwriter, moves his family from Hollywood to upstate New York. Phil hopes the change will allow him to spend more time with his wife and kids and work on the novel he's always dreamed of writing.

Settling into an old mansion locals call the Kessler Place, the Hastingses are just starting to feel at home when strange things begin to happen. The family cat is torn to pieces by a vicious animal, and Phil's daughter, Gabbie, is attacked by a mysterious assailant.

Puzzled, Phil turns to Mark Blackman, an expert on psychic phenomena, for help. Mark's investigations reveal that the Kessler Place and the area surrounding it are linked to a pact between an ancient mystical order and a group of transplanted European fairies.

While most of these supernatural creatures are not evil, some, like the Fool and his servant, the Bad Thing, seem to have a vendetta against the Hastingses. Events reach a crisis point when the pair kidnaps Patrick, Phil's eight-year-old son, and replaces him with a changeling.

Fortunately, the Fool has not counted on the courage and determination of Patrick's twin brother, Sean. Setting out in pursuit, Sean follows the abductors back to their lair in the heart of Faerie. But to save his beloved sibling, Sean must outwit the Fool and find a way home before he and Patrick become trapped forever.

Goat-like foot

PHYSICAL CHARACTERISTICS One of the Faerie creatures residing near the Kessler Place, the White Lady is a beautiful siren who lures men to their doom. Originally from the dense forests of Eastern Europe, she often travels with two identical sisters.

Able to pass for human at first glance, the White Lady's pale gown conceals her animal-like feet. Haunting secluded areas, she entices men into her clutches, then makes love to them until they expire.

WHITE LADY

SOURCE:
Faerie Tale
Raymond E. Feist

THE WORLD Described as a "jungle" and a place where "the weak are eaten," New York City is no stranger to bad press. But even the Big Apple's worst detractors have no idea how much truth there is in those remarks.

For New York is home to a highly evolved lupine species known as Wolfen, who possess a high degree of intelligence and superkeen senses. Urban predators who nest in slum areas and feed on those who will not be missed, the Wolfen have kept their presence hidden for centuries. From the burned-out tenements of the South Bronx, to the wooded paths of Central Park, they prowl the streets of the city by night, searching for victims.

A Wolfen's paw

HISTORY Investigating a double murder in Brooklyn, a pair of detectives accidentally discover that the killings were committed by Wolfen. Stalked by the creatures, the officers, in order to survive, must convince a skeptical world the Wolfen exist.

PHYSICAL CHARACTERISTICS *Canis Lupus sapiens,* or Wolfen, have larger skulls and more expressive faces than any other species in their genus. Their highly dexterous paws allow them to manipulate handles and contain razor-sharp claws.

Guided by an acute sense of smell, Wolfen are able to track prey over great distances. Social by nature, they live in packs consisting of four or five individuals. Each of these units is governed by a designated leader, selected on the basis of ability.

Wolfen have no fear of humanity, but recognize the advantages of keeping their existence secret. Pack members consume their own dead to prevent the corpses from being found.

Roughly the size of timber wolves, Wolfen move with blinding speed. Their dusky coats enable them to blend into shadow and remain virtually invisible.

While their minds operate differently from ours, Wolfen are capable of strategic planning and have their own complex language. This combination of intelligence and awesome physical prowess makes them the deadliest predators on earth.

Lateral view of Wolfen showing flattened profile

WOLFEN

SOURCE:
The Wolfen
Whitley Strieber

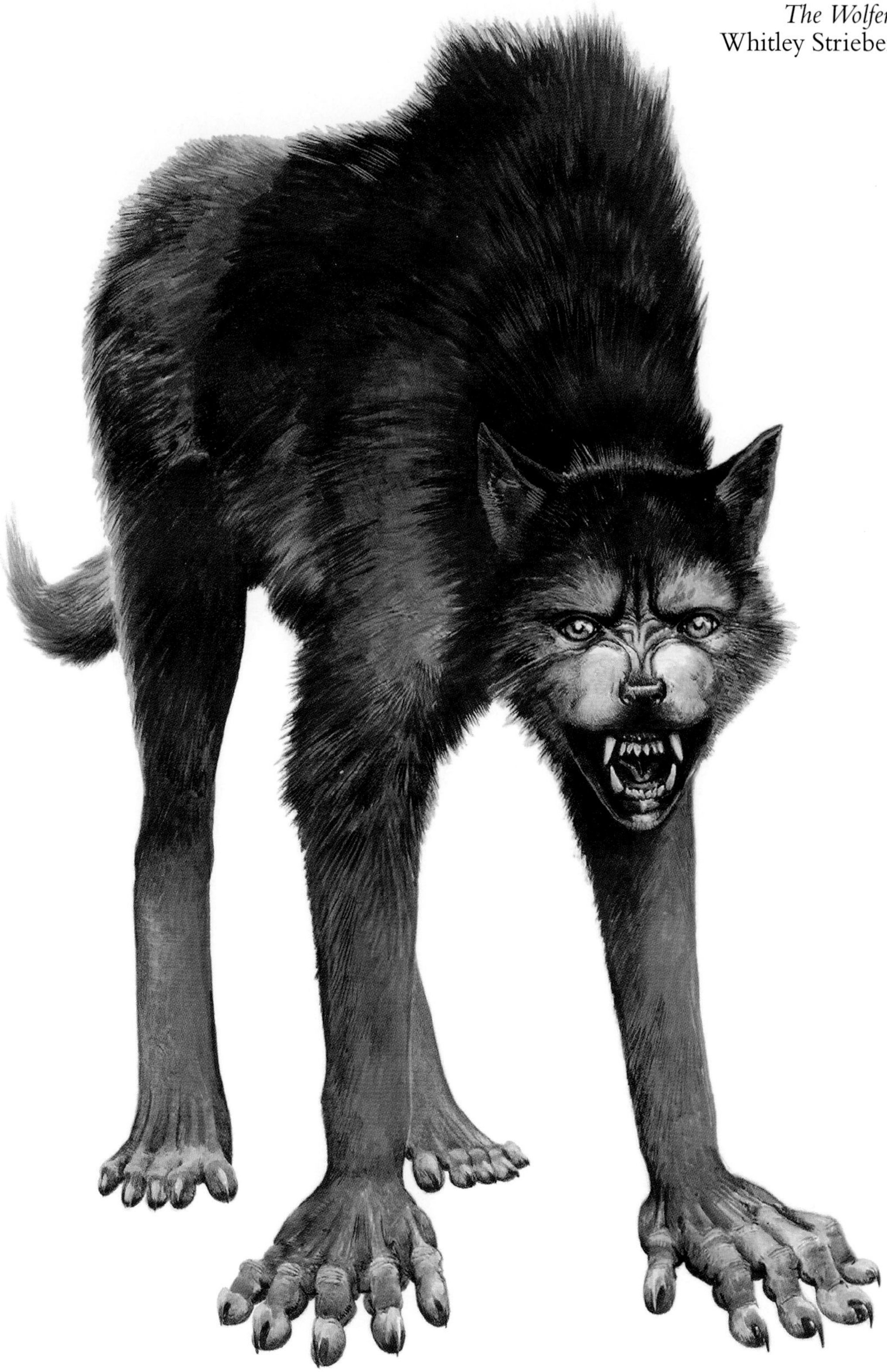

This folio of pencil drawings is taken directly from Wayne Barlowe's sketchbook. Here are his preparatory renderings, notes, and early studies of many of the fantasy creatures in this book, as well as preliminary sketches for his upcoming project, *Pilgrimage To Hell*.

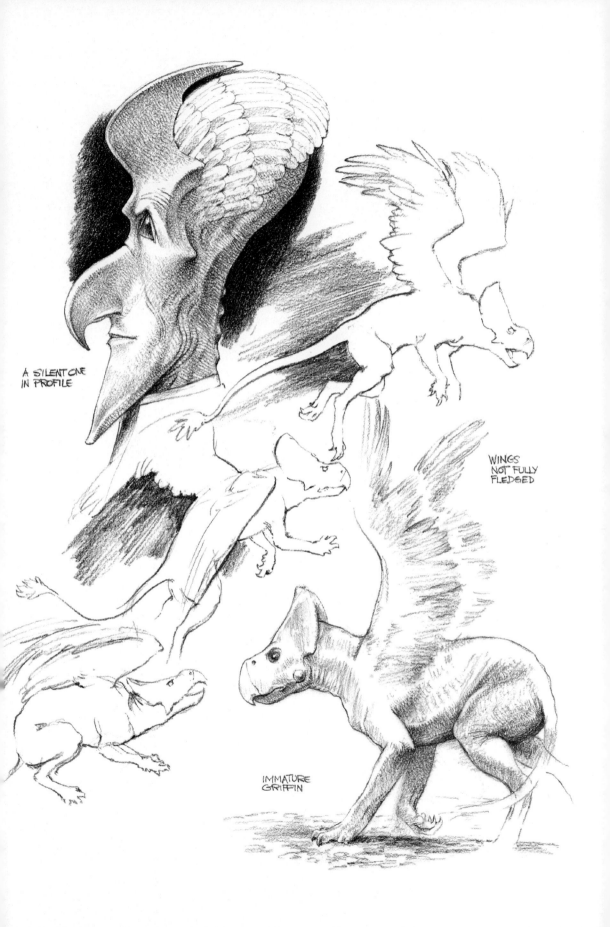

A SILENT ONE
IN PROFILE

WINGS
NOT FULLY
FLEDGED

IMMATURE
GRIFFIN

SWINE-THING SEEN
IN THE GARDEN

CAN RUN UPRIGHT OR
ON ALL FOURS

Carcë

BRAN MAK MORN

A PICT

A "WORM"

KEROWYN

RUM JHAELEN IRSEI

GRENDEL APPROACHES HEOROT

THE DRAGON

THE DRAGON TRANSFORMING

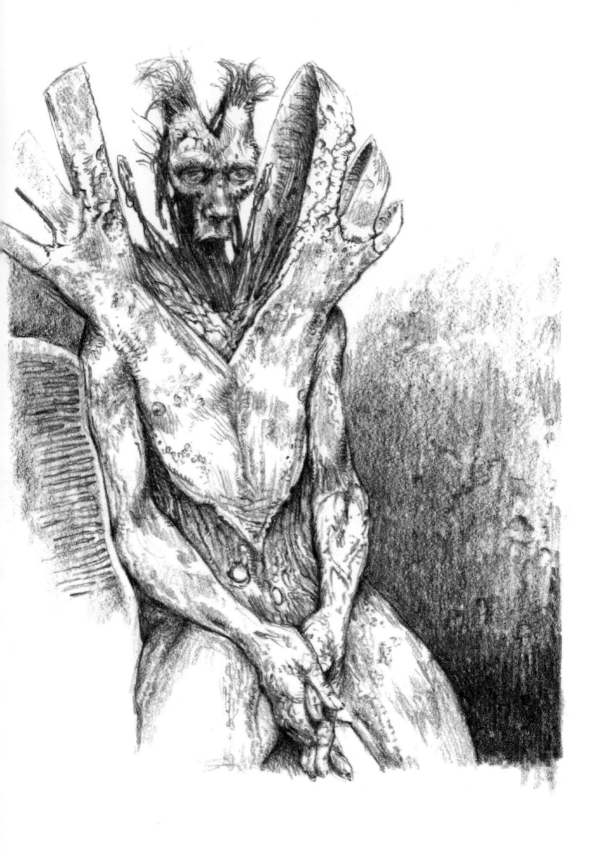

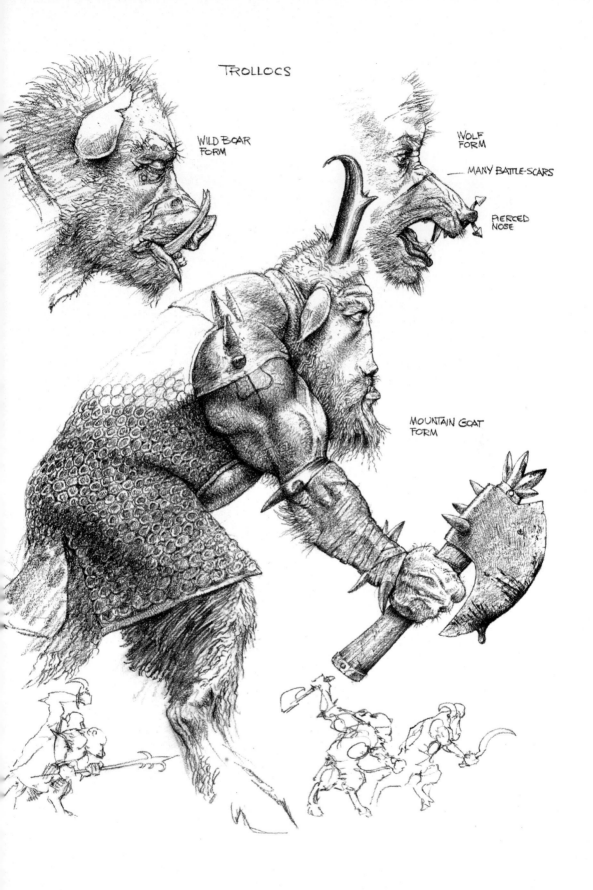

TROLLOCS

WILD BOAR
FORM

WOLF
FORM

MANY BATTLE-SCARS

PIERCED
NOSE

MOUNTAIN GOAT
FORM

PSAMMEAD GRANTING A WISH

GEK A GEK

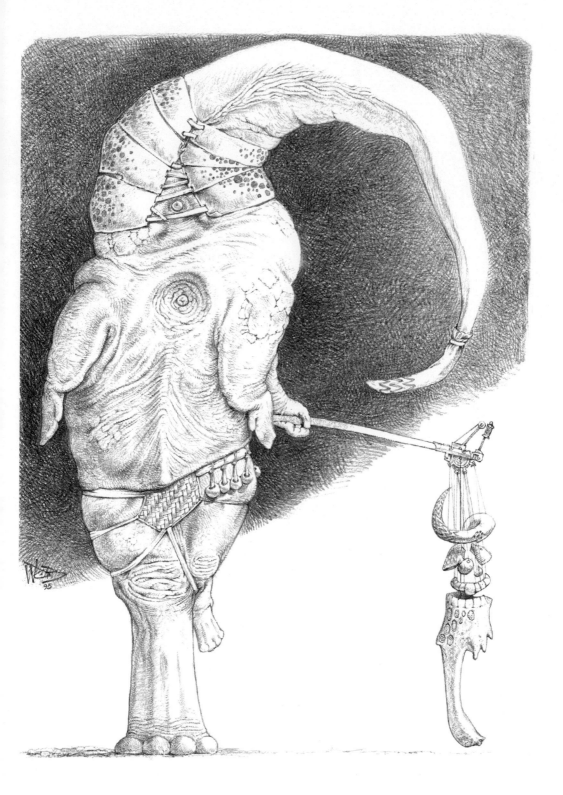

A MONOD WITH HIS EGO-PUPPET

ONE
HINGE
OR TWO?

MACHINE BEAST

REARING ALZABO

SHORT
HORN

HORSE MANDIBLE

UNICORN MANDIBLE

NOTE PROCESSES

WOOLLY
COAT

JUVENILE UNICORN

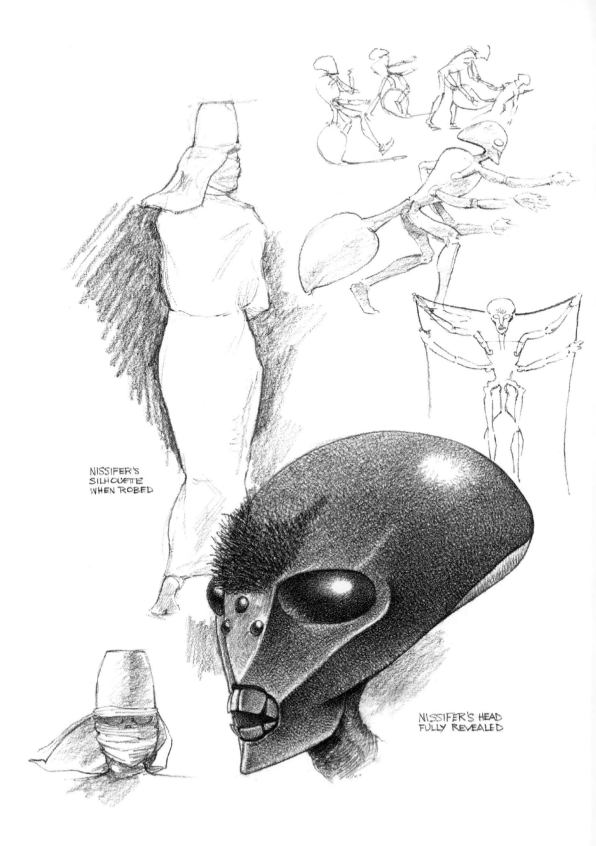

NISSIFER'S
SILHOUETTE
WHEN ROBED

NISSIFER'S HEAD
FULLY REVEALED

GUG
PLACE OF
WORSHIP

GUG HAND
COMPARED TO HUMAN
DRAWN TO SCALE

GUG MINUS HAIRY COAT
TO SHOW UNDERLYING
MUSCLES

WOLFEN

ANYANWU
IN MID-TRANSFORMATION

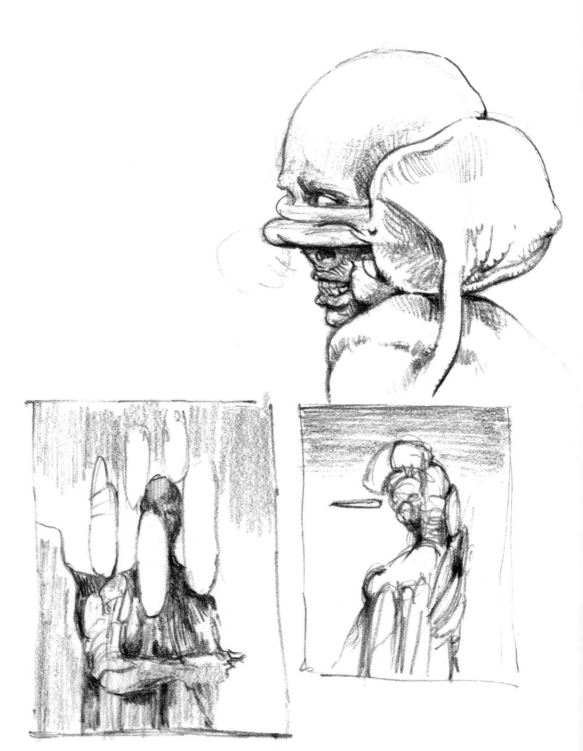

A BAITAL
IN FLIGHT

AFRIT SEEN
ATOP MINARET

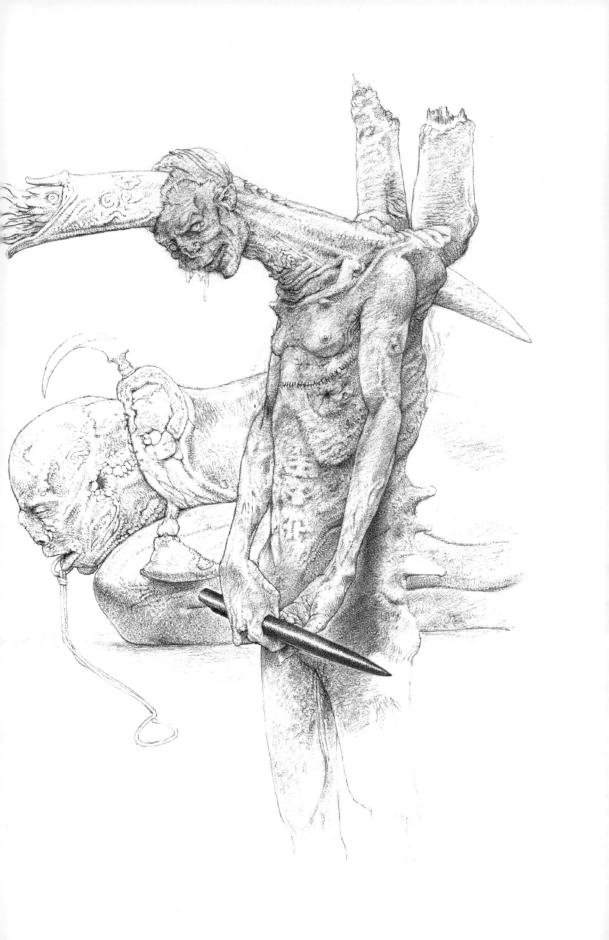